FLORIDA FRUIT

Photography
(unless otherwise indi(
by LEWIS S. MAXV

CONTENTS

For information about our books refer to the back cover.

LEWIS S. MAXWELL, Publisher
6230 Travis Boulevard
Tampa, Florida 33610

Manufactured in the United States of America

PREFACE

For many years the authors of this book have been fascinated by the many delicious fruit that grow well in Florida. However, information regarding the growing and care of Florida fruit in the home grounds was not readily available. This book has been written to fill this need.

The fruit included in this book are pleasant to eat as fresh fruit, will grow well in Florida, and are available from at least some nurseries. (**We cannot help you locate plants. Consult the nurserymen in your area or your local Agricultural Extension Service.**)

This book contains a picture and descriptive page on most of the fruit. There are also special articles to help you in such matters as the choosing, planting, caring for, and picking of these fruit. The article on the fertilization and care of citrus may be used as a guide for other fruit.

Since the flavors of these fruit vary greatly, it would be best to taste test them before planting any in your yard. Another thing that you should be aware of is that the fruit from seedlings vary to the extent that some are good to eat while others of the same species are worthless. Because of this, you should buy young plants that have been layered, grafted, or budded from plants producing superior fruit. Other reasons for buying these types of plants are that they make better shaped plants and they produce fruit in from one half to one third of the time required by seedlings.

Other factors involved in choosing fruit for your home grounds include hardiness to cold, salt tolerance, soil conditions, and size of the mature plant. A plant's mature size may vary in different areas of the State. Also, its cold hardiness may vary depending on its age, health, variety, location, number of hours at or below freezing, the weather prior to freezing temperatures, etc.

In some cases specific pesticides are not listed in this book due to ever changing regulations concerning their use. Consult your local Agricultural Extension Service or the pesticide label for current specific recommendations.

We thank Dr. J. A. Mortensen of the Florida Grape Laboratory at Leesburg; Dr. C. W. Campbell of the Homestead Experiment Station; Dr. W. B. Sherman, Fruit Crops Department, University of Florida; Mr. T. J. Anderson, Sr.; Mr. Gene Joyner, Extension Ornamental Horticulturist, Palm Beach County; Dr. C. A. Anderson, Lake Alfred Citrus Experiment Station; and the many others who have cheerfully helped us with this book.

We thank Mr. Gene Joyner, Extension Ornamental Horticulturist, Palm Beach County, for his help with the revisions in this book.

We are indebted to Mr. Warren O. Johnson and the Federal-State Agricultural Weather Service for the map on the cover of this book.

We have tried to make this a useful book, and we hope that it will encourage more people to grow and enjoy Florida fruit.

Lewis S. Maxwell

ISBN 0-9613240-5-8

AUTHORS

Dr. A. H. Krezdorn, M.S., U. of F.; Ph.D., Texas A. and M. University

Dr. Krezdorn was Professor Emeritus, Department of Fruit Crops, University of Florida, and an international consultant. He served on the Texas A. and M. University faculty for nine years, the University of Florida Citrus Experiment Station for three years and was Chairman, Department of Fruit Crops for fifteen years.

He was a Fellow and past President of the American Society for Horticultural Science and Honorary member of the Florida State Horticultural Society.

Mr. Albert A. Will, Jr., B.L.A., M.S., U. of F.

Mr. Will is a graduate landscape architect and botanist turned teacher. He is known throughout south Florida, both for his horticultural lectures and for being the founder of the first two-year horticulture program in Florida at the Junior College of Broward County.

Mr. Will has appeared on both radio and TV, and he is an active member of many national and community professional horticultural societies. He is also a co-founder of the Broward County Bromeliad Society. He has taught numerous evening adult education courses in landscape design and plant identification and has been working "in plants" professionally since 1952.

Mr. Eric V. Golby, F.R.H.S.

Mr. Golby was Production and Sales Manager of Reasoner's Tropical Nurseries, Inc. at Bradenton, Florida. He is well known in Florida because of his wide knowledge of tropical and subtropical plants. He is a fourth generation professional gardener. Both his father and grandfather were well known as hybridizers and originators of various new plants.

Fellow of The Royal Horticultural Society.

Mr. Lewis S. Maxwell, B.S.A., U. of F.

Mr. Maxwell is a professional entomologist and plant pathologist as well as an expert photographer. He is the publisher of the *Florida Garden Guide*, a bimonthly publication, that is purchased by the better garden supply dealers, termite specialists, horticultural spraymen, and nurseries to give as a free service to their customers.

Companion gardening books to *Florida Fruit* are his books *Florida Vegetables*, *Florida Flowers (Annuals and Bulbs)*, *Florida Plant Selector*, *Florida Trees and Palms*, *Florida Insects*, and *Florida Lawns and Gardens*.

BUDDING AND GRAFTING YOUNG FRUIT TREES

By A. H. Krezdorn

Most fruit plants are propagated by graftage (budding and grafting) because seedlings do not produce plants exactly like those from which the seeds are taken, they bear fruit sooner than seedlings and because a desired variety **(scion variety)** can be budded or grafted onto seedlings with root systems **(rootstocks or stocks)** resistant to certain soil diseases, insects and nematodes or which are tolerant of such soil conditions as salinity or poor drainage. Also, certain stocks may improve the size, yield and quality of fruit and the vigor and cold hardiness of the scion variety.

Some fruit trees can not be propagated by graftage (coconut, date, banana) because they do not have a continuous meristematic layer (cambium) between the bark and wood. Cells of the cambium layer are capable of dividing and differentiating (changing) into other types of cells and tissues and of producing a wound tissue called callus which is what unites buds and grafts with the stock. Some plants (papayas) can be grafted, but it is difficult to obtain proper plant material.

Genetic limits of graftage. Plants are placed in categories such as varieties (cultivars), species, genera, tribes, families, etc. that indicate their relationship. Varieties within a species, closely related, are nearly always compatible. Species within genera, such as plum or peach, are commonly but not always compatible. Genera within the same tribe are usually not compatible, and it is unusual to graft between tribes. Successful graftage of citrus varieties between genera and even sub-tribes, some of which would not, to a layperson, faintly resemble citrus, is, however, common. Some combinations form weak unions that later break off.

Methods of graftage. There are only a few basic methods but many variations. The method used is determined by whether the bark is slipping (can be peeled off from the wood), the size (diameter) of the stock to be used, the thickness of the bark and personal preference.

The T-bud is by far the most common method used commercially for budding seedling rootstocks of pencil-size diameter. A T or an inverted T (⊥) cut (the matrix) is made on the rootstock a few inches above ground level and the bark flaps of the T pulled back from the wood. A ½ to 1 inch long shield-shaped piece of bark with a small sliver of wood and a bud **(collectively the budeye)** is cut from the scion budstick and inserted under the bark, pointed end first. The cuts are reversed from the inverted T (⊥) which is popular in Florida and a little easier to use. The entire budeye and matrix are wrapped with a polyethylene plastic strip, starting at the top of the T and wrapping downward in an overlapping spiral. The wrap is secured at the bottom by slipping the end of the tape under the last spiral and pulling it tight. Wrap firmly, not loosely, to keep the budeye tightly placed against the stock and to prevent drying out. There are cambial cells both on the underside of the bark flaps and covering the woody cylinder against which the underside of the budeye is pressed. A V-shaped line of cambial cells is exposed on the budeye's underside. The cambial areas proliferate callus rapidly, the callus of the budeye intermingling and melding with that of the stock to make initial union. Certain of these cells differentiate into vascular (conductive) tissue to furnish water and food to the bud. A cambium layer is also differentiated in the callus union that becomes continuous with that of the rootstock. Union is complete in 2 weeks at which time the plastic tape is removed and the scion bud **forced** to grow by cutting off the rootstock portion above the united scion bud. If done in the fall, the bud is not forced until the following spring. As this bud sends up a shoot, it is tied to a stake to prevent breakage. All rootstock shoots should be rubbed off the stock below the bud union as soon as they arise.

INVERTED T

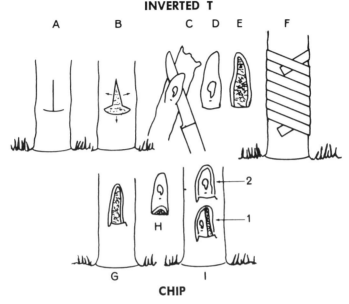

CHIP

Fig. 1. Diagrammatic sketches of inverted T-bud top and chip bud bottom. A, cuts on stock; B, flaps of matrix lifted to accept scion bud; C, scion bud being cut off; D, front view of scion budeye; E, back of budeye, shaded area indicating wood and the line just exterior to it the cambium; F, bud inserted and wrapped; G, matrix of chip bud; H, front view of scion budeye which differs from the T only in the beveled edge at the base; I-1, budeye inserted into a larger matrix, note one side matches; I-2, budeye inserted into matrix of same size. Wrapping is the same as for the T.

The chip bud can be used when the bark is not slipping on either rootstock or scion, on stocks with slightly thicker and thinner bark than suitable for the T-bud, on slightly larger stocks and on varieties having buds that do not lend themselves to the T-bud. Commercial budders can complete many more T-buds than chip buds in a day but speed is not important to the gardener.

To make the chip bud cut a ½ to 1 inch long shallow chip of bark and wood out of a smooth area of the rootstock. Make one long downward cut and then a short downward cut at the base which leaves a short bark flap. A chip as near the same size and shape as removed from the stock and with a bud is cut from the budstick and inserted into the rootstock replacing the chip removed there. It is tied, forced and handled as is the T-bud except the wrapping is left on a week longer. Never use a scion chip larger than the one on the stock. When a smaller scion chip is used, which is frequent, place it so the bark and cambium match that of one side of the bark and cambium of the matrix and not in the center of the matrix. If the difference in chip sizes is great it is well to unwrap after 2 to 3 weeks and rewrap without covering the bud.

5

Grafting differs from budding in that scion pieces with 2 or more buds are used instead of one bud. **A modified cleft or wedge graft** is widely used on avocados in Florida. Seeds are planted in pots or plastic bags from summer to October, and the trunks of the young seedlings are cut off a few inches above soil level when about ¼ inch in diameter. The stock is split (cut) down the center 1 to 1½ inches with a very sharp knife or razor blade. Four to five inch terminal portions of small branches with plump dormant buds (not elongating or flowering) are used as the scion grafts. Starting at the side of a bud, two 2-inch cuts down each side of the basal portion of the scion graft are made to form a wedge that is inserted into the cleft on the stock. Starting at the bottom, the completed graft is wrapped in overlapping spirals with a plastic strip until it covers the top of the stock and lower part of the scion graft above the stock, leaving about an inch of the terminal portion of the graft exposed. Remove plastic strips when constriction due to increase in diameter of the stock is evident. The wedge graft is self-forcing because the rootstock top is cut off at the time of grafting.

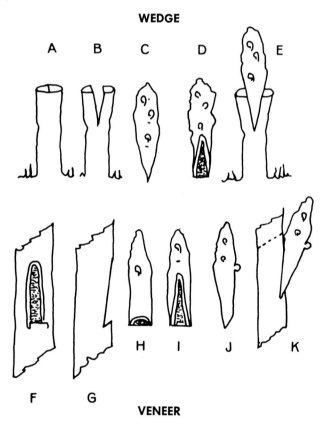

WEDGE

A B C D E

F G

H I J K

VENEER

Fig. 2 Diagrammatic sketches of wedge and veneer grafts. A, stock cut off at right angles; B, clefted stock; C, front view of scion graft; D, side view of scion graft; E, the cleft; F, matrix of veneer graft, note similarity to chip bud matrix; G, side view of matrix; H, I, J, front, back and side view of veneer graft, scion prepared for insertion; K, inserted graft, the dotted line indicates where rootstock will be cut off to force.

The veneer graft is commonly used on pot- or bag-grown avocado and mango seedlings ¼ to ¾ inch in diameter. The matrix is similar to that of the chip bud, 2 to 2½ inches long. Starting on the stem side opposite a bud, make a tapering cut to match the matrix and make a short wedge cut at the base to fit the basal flap of the matrix. Insert into the matrix. Starting at the bottom wrap the grafted area with a plastic strip, making certain the entire grafted area is sealed so that water cannot enter. Remove the rootstock portion above the scion graft when constriction due to growth is evident.

Graftage requires certain skills and techniques which while easily mastered are important. Learn to sharpen a knife and keep it sharp. Use a single-edged razor blade for tender tissue, such as wedge-grafted avocados, if unsuccessful with a knife. Make smooth, straight cuts in one plane, not undulating ones. Do not "dig out" concave cuts. Practice making proper cuts. Wrap carefully and firmly but not so firm as to damage tender tissue. Use plastic strips half as wide as normal when budding extremely small stocks and scions. Complete operation quickly so exposed cuts do not dry out. Do not touch cut surfaces with fingers if possible. Callus formation and union are slower in cool than in warm weather so judge removal of wrappings accordingly. When in doubt remove wraps and rewrap.

CHARACTERISTICS OF COMMON GRAFTAGE METHODS FOR NURSERY SIZE FRUIT TREES

Method	Bark must slip Stock	Scion	Stock size[1] (inches)	Best time(s) to use[2]
T-Bud	Yes	No[3]	Up to ½	Spring, Fall
Chip Bud	No	No	Up to ¾	Spring, Fall
Wedge Graft	No	No	¼ to ½	Fall, Winter
Veneer Graft	No	No	¼ to ¾	When material available

[1]Size limitations are coarse and can be exceeded to some degree in both directions.
[2]In central and southern Florida evergreen species, such as citrus and avocado, can be budded and grafted whenever material is available and plants can be protected from frost.
[3]Use buds from rounded subterminal growth for citrus, not angular terminal growth.

SUGGESTED GRAFTAGE PROCEDURES FOR VARIOUS KINDS OF FRUIT

Method[1]			
T or L	Chip	Wedge	Veneer
Apple	Apple	Mango	Avocado[4]	Atemoya[3]
Citrus	Citrus	Peach	Papaya	Avocado
Peach	Fig[2,3]	Pear		Carambola[3]
Pear	Grape[3]	Pecan		Loquat
Plum	Guava[3,5]	Persimmon		Mango
	Loquat	Plum		

[1]Suggested for convenience and high rate of success, other methods might also be successful. There are a number of miscellaneous tropical fruits not listed. When in doubt, try chip bud or veneer graft.
[2]Do not be concerned with latex flow. Usually propagated from stem cuttings.
[3]T-bud usually a complete failure.
[4]Can be T or chip budded but bud often falls off leaving only the united bark piece.
[5]Usually propagated by air layerage.

PLANTING FRUIT TREES
By A. H. Krezdorn

There are three factors involved in planting trees. These are: (1) the nature of the soil, (2) whether plants are bare rooted or container grown, and (3) whether plants are budded or grown from cuttings or air layers.

PREPARING THE PLANTING HOLE

Prepare a hole both wider and deeper than that needed to accommodate the roots. Place all the soil taken from the hole in a pile to one side or in a wheelbarrow. It is advantageous, but not absolutely necessary, to add an equal volume of acid peat or well-rotted compost to the pile. Using a shovel, mix the soil and the peat or compost thoroughly. Adding chemical fertilizer directly to the hole will usually damage the plant roots due to the high concentration of salts; however, it is advantageous, but not necessary, to add two to three cups of a low analysis fertilizer (no higher than an 8-8-8) to the pile of soil and peat and mix all of it thoroughly. The need for a thorough mixing of the soil, peat or compost and fertilizer can not be overemphasized. This mixture will be used to fill the hole into which the roots of the tree are placed. It should be retentive of water but not water-logged and fertile but not with an excess of fertilizer salts.

The soil mixture should not differ greatly in texture from the surrounding soil. Placing container-grown or balled and burlapped plants with a fine textured soil (clay) or an organic soil (muck and certain commercial soil mixes) around the roots in Florida's sandy soils results in poor growth. It is difficult to keep finer-textured and organic soils moist when surrounded by sand.

PLANTING THE TREE

If the plant is bare rooted, cut off broken roots and any exceptionally long ones that will not fit into the hole without bending.

Place a small amount of thoroughly mixed soil described above into the hole and firm it by hand. Place the root system in the hole, spreading out the roots in the directions of their growth. If a budded or grafted tree is used, make certain the tree is not placed deeper than it was in the nursery. Be particularly careful not to plant the bud union below the soil level. Fill in the hole with the soil mixture to about half its depth, water well and let settle. Then complete filling the hole with the soil mixture, water well and let settle. Add sufficient soil mixture to fill the hole.

If a rooted cutting is used, plant it three to six inches deeper than it was in the nursery. Such plants are usually shallow-rooted or rooted only on one side and tend to blow over. An alternative procedure is to plant at the nursery depth and stake.

Container-grown plants are often heavily rooted, with outer roots curling around to conform to container sides. This is undesirable. Make four, deep, equidistant cuts into the root mass with a large knife or pruning shears. Then place the root system into the hole at the proper depth and wash out the outer portion of the soil from the root system while holding the plant upright. Partially fill the hole with the soil mixture and water well to ensure soil being washed around all roots. Repeat adding soil mixture and water until the hole is filled. This procedure facilitates growth of new roots out of the congested mat of container roots and into the garden soil.

As a word of caution, deciduous fruit trees, such as pecans and peaches, are often purchased as container-grown plants when they were actually dug bare rooted and placed in a container with an artificial soil mix around them. Also, they are usually unbranched "whips" that have not been pruned. About one-half of the tops of such plants should be cut off to balance the top with the remaining root system and handled as bare rooted rather than container-grown plants.

WHY FRUIT TREES DO NOT BEAR
By A. H. Krezdorn

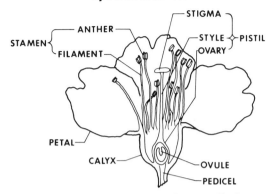

PERFECT FLOWER (DIAGRAMMATIC)

Fruit trees add to the landscape by virtue of their form, foliage or flowers, but their edible fruit is what distinguishes them from other plants. Fruit trees may produce poorly because of insects, diseases, freezes or general poor care. These problems are readily understandable. It is the failure of fruit trees to bear despite good care and favorable conditions for growth that is so frustrating. A malfunction in the sexual process of flowering and seed production is usually the cause of such unfruitfulness. Therefore, familiarity with the sexual process is necessary in order to understand problems of unfruitfulness and how to avoid them.

The sexual process begins with flowering. The individual flowers contain the male (stamen) and female (pistil) sex organs and related parts. The next step is pollination which is the transfer of pollen from the stamens to the stigmatic surface of the pistil. The pollen grains germinate on the stigmatic surface and send down pollen tubes containing sperm nuclei to the ovule, which develops into the embryo of the mature seed. The other sperm nucleus unites with other cells, the polar nuclei, which develop into food material that nourishes the developing embryo and, in some cases, produces stored food in the mature seed. The embryo is a miniature plant within the seed which develops into the tree upon being planted and germinated, thereby completing the cycle.

During pollination, pollen tube growth, sexual fertilization and seed development, there is a continuing production of hormones that stimulate the ovaries to stay attached to the tree and to enlarge and develop into mature fruit.

Some fruits, such as avocados, have one seed but others have more. Apples have 10. Seedy grapefruit have 60 to 70, and papayas have hundreds of seeds per fruit. Some but not all fruit are dependent on the full number of seeds for development of large size and shape. Apples and pears, for example, are one-sided if seeds develop only on one side. Shape is not affected by seeds in citrus but size is. For a given variety, there is an increase in **average** fruit size for every additional seed. Color and quality of some varieties are also influenced by seed content. All of this is evidence of the important stimulatory effect of sexual process leading to and including seed formation.

Seedless and nearly seedless fruits of certain species are evidence of the fact Nature abhors consistency. Varieties that set and mature fruit without the stimuli of the sexual process are termed parthenocarpic and are thereby seedless. Some parthenocarpic fruits such as bananas, pineapple, common type figs and seedless grapefruit are strongly parthenocarpic. Others such as Valencia and Hamlin oranges fruit better if they receive the stimulus of pollination, but they do not need the subsequent process of sexual fertilization. Thompson seedless grapes require sexual fertilization, but the ovules then abort and the fruit develop without seeds.

Flower formation normally occurs in 2 to 3 years when plants are propagated from fruiting plants by vegetative means such as budding. Many home fruit growers, however, start their trees from seeds taken from a fruit they happened to enjoy. Seedling trees of many species go through a long juvenile period and may take 8 to 15 years to flower and fruit. Pears, sweet oranges and pecans are examples of species with long juvenile periods. Peaches, Key lime and papaya exemplify those with very short or no juvenile period. With certain exceptions, trees produced from seeds have other disadvantages. They usually produce fruit different than the fruits from which the seeds were taken, and the fruit is usually inferior. Moreover, the root systems of such seedling trees are usually less well adapted to the soil than those of carefully selected rootstocks.

Growing trees in dense shade is also a common reason flowering is delayed or reduced in dooryard plantings. Virtually all fruit trees grown in Florida flower best when grown in full sun and poorest in dense shade.

The pollination process is best accomplished with varieties having perfect (hermaphroditic) flowers. These flowers have the male and the female organs closely associated in the same flower. Transfer of pollen often occurs mechanically by the touching of the two parts. Some kinds of fruit trees, however, have their male and female parts in separate flowers on the same tree (monoecious). Pecans and walnuts are good examples. Many, but not all, monoecious types have light pollen that is transported long distances via wind. Long rainy periods during flowering may prevent or reduce pollination and fruiting.

Still other species or varieties of some species have only male or female flowers on individual trees (dioecious). Fig varieties grown in the southern U.S., such as Celeste, Green Ischia and Brown Turkey (Everbearing), have only female flowers. They are, however, strongly parthenocarpic so lack of pollination is not a problem. The non-parthenocarpic Smyrna type figs grown in California, however, require a special wasp (Blastophaga) to carry pollen from flowers of male trees to the female flowers on other trees. Neither Blastophaga nor male trees are present in Florida. Thus, Smyrna types introduced from California shed their young fruits prior to maturity due to lack of pollination. Some papaya types have male and female plants that produce 50% male and female plants respectively when grown from seed. Cross-pollination is accomplished by a special moth. One male to about ten female plants must be present in close proximity for effective cross-pollination.

Dichogamy, a difference in time of maturity of male and female parts, occurs in some varieties. Pecan varieties have varying degrees of dichogamy, but the difference in time of maturity of the stamens and pistils usually overlap by at least a few days and wind-transplanted pollen from other varieties results in a complete overlap. Thus, only isolated trees suffer. Avocados, which have perfect flowers, exhibit a unique dichogamy. Flowers of a given variety are either type A or B. The A type sheds pollen only at a time of day when its pistils are not receptive but when those of type B are. Conversely, type B pollen is shed when A pistils are receptive but those of B are not. Bees and other insects provide for cross-pollination between A and B. Fortunately the period of pollen shedding and pistil receptivity are prolonged sufficiently in Florida so there is sufficient overlap to result in adequate fruiting. Even so, fruiting is at least improved where both A and B types are present, and isolated trees of A or B only may be unfruitful.

Sterile pollen and ovules occur commonly. Some Muscadine grapes and Bruce plum, for example, have sterile pollen and require cross-pollination by varieties with fertile pollen. Female sterile varieties must be parthenocarpic to fruit. Tahiti or Persian limes and navel oranges are both male and female sterile and parthenocarpic.

Sexual self-incompatibility, the inability of viable pollen to fertilize fertile ovules for biochemical reasons, is a widespread cause of unfruitfulness. When such varieties are parthenocarpic, seedless fruits occur unless other varieties with compatible pollen are present. In the latter case, seedy fruits develop. Thus, the weakly parthenocarpic self-incompatible Orlando, Minneola and Nova tangelos produce poor to moderate crops when isolated from other varieties. However, large crops of fruit with varying quantities of seed (0 to 40) are produced when other varieties with compatible pollen are present for cross-pollination.

All cherry and almond varieties, most plums, passion fruit, and many apple and pear varieties and some citrus varieties are sexually self-incompatible and some are cross-incompatible. Appropriate varieties for cross-pollination must be present for satisfactory fruiting. Bees are the primary pollinators, and trees must be within 30 to 40 yards of each other for maximum effectiveness. Carpenter bees (Bumblebees) are necessary to cross-pollinate passion fruit.

Florida Fruits Requiring Cross-Pollination[1,2]

Sterile pollen	Dioecious	Some blackberries
Muscadine grapes	Papaya	Passion fruit
Bruce plum	Persimmon	Feijoa
Dichogamous	**Self-incompatible**	Apples
Pecans	Most tangelos	Barbados cherry
Avocados	Blueberries	Many plums

[1]Suitable pollenizer varieties to use are too extensive to list. Check with local agricultural extension office.
[2]Cherries, almonds, apricots, raspberries, California Smyrna-type figs and other unadapted fruits are not listed.

Juvenile Period of Seedling Fruit Trees[1]

4 years or less		5 to 8 years	8 or more years	Satisfactorily grown from seed
Atemoya	Limes	Avocado	Apple	Barbados cherry
Barbados cherry	Lemons	Coconut	Grapefruit	Coconut
Blackberries	Papaya	Mango	Jaboticaba	Guava
Blueberries	Passion fruit	Persimmon	Lychee	Key lime
Carambola	Peaches	Tangelos	Mamey	Loquat
Grapes	Plums	Tangerines	Oranges	Papaya
Guava	Sugar apple		Pears	Soursop
Loquat	Soursop		Pecans	

[1]Figs, bananas and pineapple do not produce seeds without special provisions.

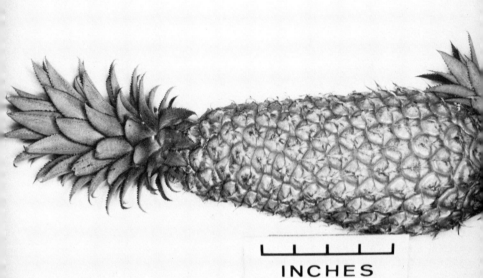

INCHES

Common Name Pineapple

Native to Tropical America

Habit of Growth Short, stiff herbaceous

Florida Height 4' **Width** 6'

Description Leaves long, thin, in rosettes, with spiny tips and usually prickly edges.

Fruit (Description & Use) Compound, fleshy, usually yellow when ripe. Outer covering rough. Eaten fresh or in pies, preserves, etc.

Flower & Season Violet or reddish on a dense head. Jan-March.

Fruit Season May-Sept. Usually after 15 to 32 months.

Soil & Moisture Improved, well-drained.

Freezes about 28°F.

pH Preference 5.5 to 6.0.

Sun or Shade Sun or partial shade.

Rate of Growth Moderate.

Salt Tolerance Fair.

Culture Set 12" to 18" apart in 20" rows. Plant so sand will not get into bud. Early spring best time to set new plants. Larger the planting piece, the sooner the fruit.

Propagation Suckers, below fruit, or ratoons that start from below ground are best. Crown from top of fruit is the poorest planting piece.

Problems Mealybugs. Nematodes are a severe problem. Plants stop growing at 55° to 60°F.

Varieties Smooth Cayenne (no spines), Red Spanish, Abakka, Natal Queen, Pernambuco (Abacaxi, Eleuthera).

PINEAPPLES

By Lewis S. Maxwell

A pineapple is one of the most delicious fruit in the world especially if picked and eaten when fresh.

The pineapple plant is damaged at 32°F. and will be killed at about 28°F. if no protection is given. However, a cover over the plants will usually save them. Pineapple plants have been saved from freezing by simply covering the buds with dead grass.

There are several varieties from which to choose. Red Spanish usually fruits in May or June. Smooth Cayenne with its almost spineless leaves fruits from July to September. Natal Queen is a good variety. It fruits from June to July, and since it produces an abundance of suckers, it is easy to propagate. Pernambuco, which usually fruits in June or July, is easy to gas and thus have fruit during the winter months. Abakka which fruits in July to September is of a good quality even though it is subject to black heart.

Weeding of pineapples is difficult because of their spiny leaves. Therefore, much effort should be put into eliminating weeds before planting. This may be done by intensive cultivation, mulching, and by use of weed killers.

A nematocide should be used prior to planting.

PINEAPPLE STALK SHOWING PLANTING PIECES

Pictured are several kinds of "planting pieces." They are:

1. Crown: This is the top section above the fruit. It is the least satisfactory as it tends to produce small fruit.

2. Slips: These are growths arising above or below the fruit but close to the fruit.

3. Suckers: These are best. They come from the stem either above or below the ground. The suckers that come from the stem below the ground are called "ratoons" or ground suckers.

These planting pieces should be cut from the mother plant and dried in the shade for about three days before planting. Do not plant them too deep. The larger the plant piece, the sooner it will produce fruit.

When planted in March, average times for producing fruit are as follows: 17 months for suckers, 26 months for slips, and 29 months for crowns.

Pineapples are usually set in early spring as soon as danger of frost is past. They are usually set from 12 to 18 inches apart. As soon as young plants are established, it is well to put some bulky organic such as well rotted compost in the buds. This will keep sand or mixed fertilizer out of the bud. Either sand or mixed fertilizer in the bud will kill the plant.

Here is a two year schedule for taking care of pineapple plants:

FIRST YEAR

They should be planted in March. A bulky organic should be placed in the buds.

Each month I pour a cupful of a solution of water soluble fertilizer into the bud of each plant. I have found this to be the most satisfactory method of feeding these plants.

In April, August, and December I spread 3 tablespoonfuls of a quality mixed fertilizer containing added essential elements and organics on the soil around each plant.

SECOND YEAR

Again, I pour a cupful of a solution of water soluble fertilizer into the bud of each plant each month.

In April and in August again fertilize the plants in the same manner as they were fertilized in the previous April.

In July gas the plants to force bloom.

Most pineapples when left alone will produce fruit from May to September. Plants can be forced to bloom by a technique called gassing. This consists of putting water in the bud and then dropping 10 to 12 grains of calcium carbide into the bud of 18 to 20 month old plants. The fruit will usually then mature in from 5 to 7 months.

In January most of the fruit should be ready to harvest. After harvest again spread fertilizer on the soil around the plants.

As soon as crops become poor, the land should be cleared. At this time it is well to spade or disc the area and treat it with a nematocide before replanting pineapples.

Mealybugs are probably the worst pest of pineapples. Spraying with Malathion will kill them. Reddish-yellow color of the leaves is a symptom of mealybug damage.

Red spiders are also pests. They can be controlled by various miticides.

Scientific Name Annona muricata   **Family** Annonaceae

Common Name Soursop   **Native to** Tropical America

Habit of Growth Small, upright tree.   **Florida Height** 20′ **Width** 15′

Description Leaves alternate, 4″ to 6″ long, leathery, very dark shiny green. Leaves have pungent odor when crushed.

Fruit (Description & Use) Large 6″ to 9″ long, yellow-green in color, and covered with fleshy spines. Flesh white. Used for custards, ices and fruit drink.

Flower & Season Large, yellowish. May onward.   **Fruit Season** June through Nov. Some fruit all year.

Soil & Moisture Rich, moist soil.   **Freezes about** 30°F.

pH Preference 5.5 to 6.5.   **Sun or Shade** Sun or partial shade.

Rate of Growth Moderate.   **Salt Tolerance** Fair on acid soil.

Culture Most tropical of the annonas. Should be mulched and irrigated.

Propagation By seeds or budding.

Problems Young plants are very tender.

Varieties Fiberless Cuban, much seedling variation. A. montana is not palatable.

Scientific Name Annona reticulata   **Family** Annonaceae

CUSTARD-APPLE

Common Name Custard-Apple
Bullocks-Heart

Native to Tropical America

Habit of Growth Small, spreading tree.

Florida Height 25' **Width** 20'

Description Leaves alternate, simple, to 8" long.
Semideciduous, sheds most of its leaves during winter.

Fruit (Description & Use) Heart-shaped, 3" to 5" in diameter. 1 to 2 pounds.
Skin brownish-red when ripe.   Eaten fresh, in custard and ices.

Flower & Season Yellowish to 1" long.   **Fruit Season** April-June.
Late spring.

Soil & Moisture Moist, well-drained.   **Freezes about** 28°F. Young trees 32°F.

pH Preference 5.0 to 7.5.   **Sun or Shade** Sun.

Rate of Growth Moderate.   **Salt Tolerance** Fair.

Culture Tree is top heavy and requires pruning. Cannot stand wet feet.

Propagation From seeds. Seedlings will fruit in 4 to 5 years.

Problems Chalcid fly.

Varieties Lindstroms, Pink Mammoth.

16

Scientific Name Annona squamosa   **Family** Annonaceae

Common Name Sugar-Apple   **Native to** Tropical America
Sweetsop

Habit of Growth Small, open tree.   **Florida Height** 15' **Width** 15'

Description Leaves alternate, 6" to 8" long, thin, and soft. Deciduous.

Fruit (Description & Use) Heart-shaped, 3" to 4" in diameter. Skin lumpy, green with bluish or white bloom. Pick fruit just before maturity.
Best as a fresh fruit. Excellent.

Flower & Season Greenish-yellow,   **Fruit Season** August-winter.
1" long. Late spring.

Soil & Moisture Good soil.   **Freezes about** 27°F.

pH Preference 7.0 to 8.0   **Sun or Shade** Sun or partial shade.

Rate of Growth Moderate.   **Salt Tolerance** Fair.

Culture Acid soils should be limed. Most satisfactory annona for South Florida.

Propagation Selected varieties are grafted or budded.

Problems Chalcid Fly. Young trees are very tender.

Varieties Seedless Brazilian & Cuban, Island Gem, Lincoln, Purple.

Scientific Name (Annona cherimola x A. squamosa)   **Family** Annonaceae

Photograph by Gene Joyner

Common Name Atemoya   **Native to** Tropical America
(cherimoya x sugar apple)

Habit of Growth Small, sprawling tree.   **Florida Height** 30′ **Width** 30′

Description Leaves alternate, simple, elliptic, ovate, or lanceolate, 4″ to 8″ long. Deciduous.

Fruit (Description & Use) Heart-shaped, 3″ to 5″ in diameter. Skin lumpy. Color yellowish-green at maturity. Flesh white, custardlike, with sweet, pleasing flavor. Seeds 10 to 40, dark.   Use as a fresh fruit.

Flower & Season Yellowish, 1¼″ to 1½″. Spring and late summer.

Fruit Season August-November.

Soil & Moisture Well-drained, fertile.

Freezes about 27°F.

pH Preference 7.0 to 8.0.

Sun or Shade Sun or partial shade.

Rate of Growth Moderate.

Salt Tolerance Fair.

Culture Likes alkaline soils. Irrigate when needed except when tree is dormant.

Propagation Selected varieties are grafted on custard apple or pond apple.

Problems Chalcid fly.

Varieties Gefner, African Pride (Kaller), Page, Bradley, Stermer, and Mammoth.

18

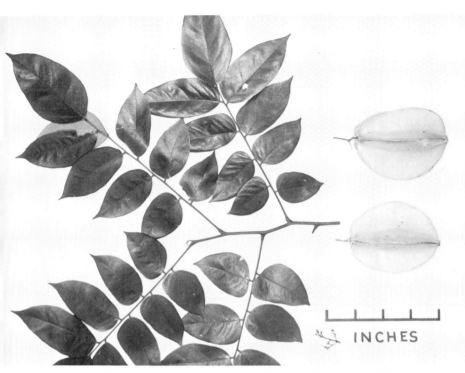

INCHES

Common Name Carambola

Habit of Growth Small, symmetrical tree.

Native to Malaya and S. E. Asia

Florida Height 25' **Width** 20'

Description Leaves compound, alternate, odd pinnate. The leaflets are larger toward the outer tip of leaf.

Fruit (Description & Use) Yellow with waxlike surface. Sides deeply ridged. Cross section of fruit is star-shaped. Borne on trunk and branches. Eaten fresh, in jams and ades.

Flower & Season Small, rose colored, fragrant. Several times during year.

Soil & Moisture Good, moist soil.

pH Preference 5.5 to 6.5.

Rate of Growth Moderate.

Fruit Season Often two to four crops. Major crops summer and fall.

Freezes about 27°F. Young trees 32°F.

Sun or Shade. Sun or semishade.

Salt Tolerance Poor.

Culture Grows well with a minimum of care. Prefers acid soils. Severely damaged by flooding. Needs minor elements.

Propagation Seedlings bear in 3 to 5 years. Superior varieties should be propagated by veneer grafting or chip budding.

Problems No serious pests.

Varieties Golden Star, Pei Sy Tao, Newcomb, Thayer, White, Starking, and others. A. bilimbi is not used as a fresh fruit.

Scientific Name (Calocarpum sapota)
Pouteria sapota

Family Sapotaceae

INCHES

Common Name Mamey Sapote. (Zapote)

Native to Central America

Habit of Growth Handsome, open tree.

Florida Height 30' **Width** 25'

Description Leaves large to 12" long, to 4" wide. Shiny green with lighter color underneath. Leaves clustered at tips of thick brittle twigs.

Fruit (Description & Use) Rough brown skin, 4" to 8" long. Pulp orange-red in color. Usually one seed but may have up to 4. Good eaten as a fresh fruit.

Flower & Season Small, whitish flowers. Oct.-Dec.

Fruit Season May-July. Flavor and color changes with climate.

Soil & Moisture Good, well-drained.

Freezes about 30°F.

pH Preference 5.5 to 8.0.

Sun or Shade Sun.

Rate of Growth Moderate.

Salt Tolerance Fair.

Culture Plants easily killed by poor drainage.

Propagation Better varieties by grafting and air layering. Because of polymorphism, 5 or more seedlings should be planted. Seed to first fruit may take 20 years or more.

Problems Scale insects.

Varieties Cuban No. 1, Magana. Green Sapote, C. viride, occasionally planted.
20

INCHES

Common Name Papaya   **Native to** Tropical America

Habit of Growth Herb with stout trunk.   **Florida Height** 15′ **Width** 7′

Description Leaves lobed, to 2′ across. Has long round petioles. Trunk not woody. Female flowers are against trunk; male flowers are in clusters on long stems. There are bisexual varieties.

Fruit (Description & Use) Melonlike. Size and shape varies, ½ to 20 pounds. Flesh yellow to orange-red. Numerous black seeds in cavity.

Breakfast or dessert fruit.

Flower & Season Yellowish-white, male and female. Bloom throughout year.

Fruit Season Best during July-Oct. Some fruit all year.

Soil & Moisture Tolerates poor soil. Easily killed by flooding.

Freezes about 31°F. Young plants tender.

pH Preference 5.5 to 7.0.

Sun or Shade Sun.

Rate of Growth Rapid.

Salt Tolerance Poor.

Culture Should be mulched to partially alleviate nematode problem. Plants live 2 to 3 years. Make new plantings annually for replacements.

Propagation From seeds grown in pots. Plant at least 3 seeds. Remove most male plants when flowers appear.

Problems Papaya fruit fly—bagging fruit is the only control. Papaya viruses. Nematodes are a serious problem.

Varieties The Homestead Experiment Station has developed some selections resistant to papaya viruses.

21

INCHES

Common Name Karanda

Native to India.

Habit of Growth Sprawling shrub.

Florida Height 10' **Width** 10'

Description Leaves, shiny, opposite, 1" to 2½" long. Spiny with the spines seldom branched. Milky sap. Good for foundation planting or protective hedge.

Fruit (Description & Use) Fruit ½" to ¾" in diameter, purplish-black. Usually in clusters. Seed relatively large.   Eaten fresh; preserves

Flower & Season Fragrant, whitish, ¾" across. March to Sept.

Fruit Season May to Oct.

Soil & Moisture Well-drained soil.

Freezes about 25°F.

pH Preference 5.5 to 7.0.

Sun or Shade Sun or Semishade.

Rate of Growth Rapid.

Salt Tolerance Good.

Culture Grows well on poor dry soil. Likes good soil.

Propagation Quite variable from seed. Propagation usually from selected seedlings. Also propagated from cuttings and by marcottage.

Problems No serious pests.

Varieties Carissa edulis — much like C. carandas. Some prefer it to carandas. Carissa grandiflora — larger bush with poorer fruit.

22

Scientific Name Carya illinoensis   **Family** Juglandaceae

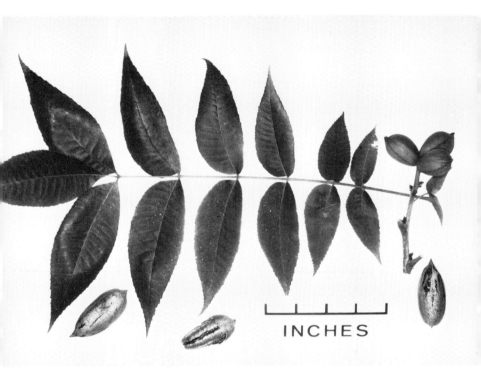

INCHES

Common Name Pecan   **Native to** S. E. U. S. A.

Habit of Growth Large, upright tree   **Florida Height** 35 to 50' **Width** 30 to 50'

Description Leaves compound, odd pinnate leaflets to 7" long. Wood hard and strong. Deciduous.

Fruit (Description & Use) Nuts smooth, light brown. Nuts are borne on current season's growth, terminal.   Eaten fresh and in desserts.

Flower & Season Catkins, male, on year old growth. Spring-mainly in March.

Fruit Season Fall (Oct-Nov.)

Freezes about Hardy.

Soil & Moisture Well-drained soil.

Sun or Shade Full sun.

pH Preference 5.5 to 6.5.

Rate of Growth Slow.

Salt Tolerance Poor.

Culture The soil pH should be maintained between 5.5 to 6.5. A mature tree should receive 30 to 50 pounds of an 8-8-8 fertilizer each year.

Propagation Budding or grafting. Takes 5 years to bear. Single trees do not set as heavy a crop as when several are within 100 feet.

Problems Needs zinc sprays for proper growth.

Varieties Curtis, Desirable.

INCHES

Common Name White Sapote   **Native to** Central America

Habit of Growth Open, evergreen tree.   **Florida Height** 40′   **Width** 40′

Description Leaves palmately compound. Bark rough and thick with conspicuous lenticels. Branches irregular, relatively brittle.

Fruit (Description & Use) Light yellow when ripe, 1½″ to 4″ in diameter. Flesh creamy-white. 1 to 6 large seeds.   Eaten fresh or in sherbets.

Flower & Season Small, greenish-yellow. Jan.-Feb. on new wood.

Fruit Season May-June. May fruit till Nov.

Soil & Moisture Rich soil.

Freezes about 24°F. Young trees 26°F.

pH Preference 5.5 to 7.0.

Sun or Shade Sun.

Rate of Growth Moderate.

Salt Tolerance Fair.

Culture When picked mature, green fruit will ripen with no loss in quality. Dormancy caused by cool winters increases fruiting. Withhold water while dormant or fruiting will be scarce.

Propagation Better varieties are veneer grafted, chip budded, or air layered.

Problems Minerals deficient in alkaline soil.

Varieties Dade, Blumenthal, Coleman, Maltby, Everbearing, Pike and others. Woolyleaf White Sapote, Casimiroa tetrameria, is preferred by some.

Scientific Name Chrysophyllum cainito   **Family** Sapotaceae

INCHES

Common Name Star-Apple   **Native to** Tropical America

Habit of Growth Beautiful, evergreen tree.   **Florida Height** 35' **Width** 35'

Description Leaves simple, alternate, dark green above and silky golden-brown underneath.

Fruit (Description & Use) Roundish, 2½" to 3" diameter. Some varieties are purple skinned, others green. Flesh white, sweet.   Very good eaten fresh

Flower & Season Small, purplish-white July to Oct.   **Fruit Season** Feb. to May.

Soil & Moisture Rich, well-drained.   **Freezes about** 29°F.

pH Preference 6.0 to 7.5.   **Sun or Shade** Sun.

Rate of Growth Moderate.   **Salt Tolerance** Poor.

Culture Plant grows well in either humid or semi-arid conditions. Quite wind resistant.

Propagation Seedlings take 6 to 10 years or more to bear. Better varieties can be air layered or grafted on seedlings.

Problems No serious pests. Young trees are very tender.

Varieties Haitian, Purple and Yellow Green.

Scientific Name Citus aurantifolia   **Family** Rutaceae

INCHES

Common Name Lime
Key Lime.

Native to Malaya, India.

Habit of Growth Small, thorny tree.   **Florida Height** 15' **Width** 10'

Description Leaves small; petiole has narrow wings. Evergreen. Leaves when crushed have an aromatic lime fragrance.

Fruit (Description & Use) Oval, thin-skinned and smooth, to 2'' across. Usually used while skin is still green. Very acid. Seedy.
Used in drinks, on sea food or in pies.

Flower & Season White, a small orange blossom. Late spring.

Fruit Season Late fall - spring.

Soil & Moisture Well-drained soil.

Freezes about 30°F.

pH Preference 5.5 to 8.0.

Sun or Shade Sun.

Rate of Growth Moderate.

Salt Tolerance Good.

Culture Limes and lemons should be treated like other citrus.

Propagation Come true from seeds or are easily grown from mature wood cuttings.

Problems Lime anthracnose, Diplodia limb dieback, and Phytophthora foot rot. See article on citrus for other problems.

Varieties The Persian Lime (Tahiti) is probably a hybrid. It stands more cold.

CITRUS FOR FLORIDA HOMES

GRAPEFRUIT

There are now red, pink, or white grapefruits available. Some have seeds, while some are seedless. Check carefully when you buy a young tree and be sure you get the kind you and your family will appreciate the most. That one will be the best for you.

TEMPLE ORANGE

This is a loose skinned, mandarin type orange that matures from January to March. It has highly colored orange peel and flesh. It is one of the best flavored of Florida's oranges, and it should be considered by anyone who wants an orange tree. This is a tangor—a probable cross between an orange and a tangerine.

TANGELO

There are several kinds of these highly flavored, loose skinned oranges. Most of them are at their best from December to March. They are a cross between a tangy tangerine and a refreshingly tart grapefruit. Both the peel and the flesh are highly colored.

TANGERINE

This is the original loose skinned citrus fruit. It has a rich, sweet flavor and a spicy aroma. The skin and flesh are deep orange to red in color. The fruit is smaller than the tangelo and tends to dry out if left on the tree too long.

PINEAPPLE ORANGE

This is one of Florida's "old stand-by" oranges. This orange ripens in midseason (December to February). It is a good size and has some seeds. Its flesh is deep orange in color and is very popular because of its juicy sweetness. It and the Valencia have a light skin which is different from the previous oranges.

VALENCIA ORANGE

This is a very popular, late orange (March to July). It is a good size and is oval shaped with a smooth, thin skin. It has only a few seeds. Because of its rich flavor and aroma, this is probably Florida's best orange for juice.

Pictures through the courtesy of the Florida Citrus Commission, Lakeland, Florida.

BRIEF DESCRIPTION OF CITRUS VARIETIES
By A. H. Krezdorn

SWEET ORANGE

HAMLIN—October-January, seedless, smooth peel, poor color, good juice.

PARSON BROWN—October-December, seedy, pebbly peel, good juice.

NAVEL—October-January, seedless, thick peel, excellent for eating out of hand, poor for juice.

PINEAPPLE—December-February, seedy, excellent color and juice.

QUEEN—Similar to Pineapple.

VALENCIA—March-July, seedless, superior color and juice quality.

Note: Seedless indicates 0-6 seeds; all oranges can be eaten out of hand but flesh texture and flavor make Navel superior for this purpose.

GRAPEFRUIT

DUNCAN—Extremely seedy, white flesh.

MARSH—Seedless, white flesh.

PINK MARSH—Seedless, pink flesh, no peel blush.

REDBLUSH (RED MARSH)—seedless, red flesh, red peel blush.

STAR RUBY—seedless, intensely red flesh, red peel blush.

Note: All grapefruit varieties can be harvested October through June but quality is best after December.

MANDARINS AND THEIR HYBRIDS

SATSUMA (S)—October-December, seedless, high color, low flavor, extremely cold hardy.

PONKAN (A)—October-November, seedy, upright growth, very loose peel, low acid, high flavor.

ROBINSON (A, P)—September-November, variable seediness, good quality.

PAGE (S,P)—October-December, variable seediness, small fruit, superior flavor.

NOVA TANGELO (P)—October-December, variable seediness, pebbly peel, less juicy than Orlando but better flavor.

ORLANDO TANGELO (P)—October-December, variable seediness, quality best in November.

DANCY (A)—December-January, seedy, puffy peel, high flavor.

MINNEOLA (A,P,S)—January-February, variable seediness, large bell-shaped fruit, superb flavor.

TEMPLE (S)—January-March, seedy, superb flavor, cold tender.

MURCOTT (HONEY ORANGE) (A,S)—February-April, seedy, excessive crops may cause dieback.

Note: Letter in brackets signify: A, alternate year fruiting; P, need for cross-pollination; S, need for annual scab disease control.

LIMES AND LEMONS

TAHITI (PERSIAN) LIME—Large, seedless green fruit; tree relatively thornless.

KEY (MEXICAN, WEST INDIAN) LIME—Small, yellow fruit with few seeds, distinctive flavor; tree thorny, a thornless variety yields less.

MEYER LEMON—Large, seedless, yellow fruit; tree thorny and cold hardy; no scab.

EUREKA TYPE—Lemons of the Eureka or lemon types are too thorny and subject to scab disease to recommend.

PONDEROSA LEMON—Huge, yellow fruit but good juice, low yields.

Note: Only the Meyer is sufficiently hardy for central Florida except in protected locations; Key lime suited only for Keys and warmest parts of south Florida, and lime anthracnose limits yields outside the Keys. Limes and lemons fruit almost continuously; main crop of Meyer is fall and winter while that of limes is spring to fall.

MISCELLANEOUS

NAGAMI (OBLONG) and MEIWA (KUMQUATS)—October-February, small-fruited, with thick sweet peel; tree quite cold hardy, dwarfish, ornamental.

CALAMONDIN—October-January, small deep orange, acid fruit, upright tree growth, ornamental.

PUMMELOS—Large, thick-peeled, grapefruit-like fruit with drier sweeter flesh good for salads; more cold tender than grapefruit.

CITRONS—Large, thick-peeled, dry flesh, cold tender, used candied peel. The Etrog variety is used in Jewish religious rites.

Note: There are many other hybrid fruits and oddities sometimes grown but too numerous to mention. These include limequats (lime x kumquat), citrange-quats (limes x kumquat x trifoliate orange), many tangelos (grapefruit x tangerine) and acidless forms of limes, lemons, and oranges too numerous to describe here.

CITRUS FOR FLORIDA HOMES

Citrus is a beautiful evergreen, ornamental tree that produces large crops of delicious fruits with a wide variety of flavors. The cold hardiest types, such as satsuma and kumquats, can be grown in north Florida. Even more tender types can be grown there in especially warm locations. The best area for citrus lies south of Ocala; however, citrus is occasionally exposed to freeze damage even in the warmest regions.

Some citrus, such as calamondin and kumquats, are primarily used for their ornamental value, but their fruit is useful. Calamondin is an excellent acid fruit for pies and drinks while kumquats are used in preserves and marmalades. Kumquats, calamondin and Meyer lemon also do well as potted or tubbed specimens.

It is best to purchase good nursery trees which will usually be budded on rootstocks. Sour orange, Cleopatra mandarin, Swingle citrummelo and trifoliate orange all induce maximum cold hardiness, best fruit quality and high resistance to foot rot.

Sour orange is a good, all-purpose stock. It is susceptible to tristeza virus, but this has not been a major problem in dooryard trees.

Rough lemon was once used to induce large fruit sizes and high yields and for extremely weak, sandy soils; however, it is no longer readily available due to susceptibility to blight disease. Volkamer lemon is a good alternative stock that is available. Carrizo citrange is second only to sour orange in use. Trees on these stocks are more sensitive to cold than those on sour orange.

Cleopatra mandarin is widely used for Temple, tangelos and most mandarins; however, trifoliate orange is preferred for satsuma.

Trifoliate orange and its hybrids (Carrizo and Swingle) should not be used on the limestone rock soils of Dade County because of their sensitivity to calcareous soils.

Macrophylla, a lime-like fruit, is an excellent stock for lemons and limes, except for Meyer which often carries the tristeza virus to which this stock is sensitive.

Meyer lemon and calamondin are often propagated as rooted cuttings and Tahiti as air layers. Citrus varieties should not be grown from seeds, even though most come true from seed, except when used for rootstocks because it usually will take many years for seedlings to come into bearing.

Labels on trees at garden centers often do not indicate the rootstock. Insist on identifying the rootstock. The best assurance of a good tree is to purchase it from a reputable source.

Citrus does best in full sun but will tolerate partial shade. Twenty to twenty-five feet of space is needed between trees unless the grower is prepared to keep them in bounds with pruning after trees begin to crowd. Citrus responds well to shearing back the sides and tops as well as to selectively removing branches. Twelve to fifteen feet between trees is minimal even with pruning.

Citrus is tolerant of a wide range of soil pH but 6.0 to 6.5 is best. Acid soils below pH 6.0 should be corrected by liming.

Citrus will not tolerate poorly drained soils, and care should be taken to avoid them or to provide adequate drainage.

It is best to plant trees at the same depth as their soil line in the nursery. Above all, avoid covering the bud union. Try to obtain trees budded at least three and preferably six or more inches above the soil line because those budded close to the ground are more prone to foot rot of the trunk just above the bud union.

FERTILIZATION AND CARE OF CITRUS
By Lewis S. Maxwell

Citrus trees are only a little more trouble to grow than shade trees. However, the thrill and pride of picking your own fresh fruit is well worth the extra effort.

Here is a program for feeding your citrus trees that will help you to have healthy trees and many delicious fruit.

After you properly plant your young citrus tree, keep an area about three feet in diameter around the young tree free of grass and weeds. This cleared area should grow with the tree keeping it about two feet beyond the tree's outer leaves.

If you use a mulch over this area, do not let the mulch touch the trunk of the tree. A heavy organic mulch against the trunk can cause foot rot.

The first year give each tree a pint (one pound) of a complete fertilizer such as a citrus special or a 6-6-6 containing natural organics, 3 units of magnesium plus added essential elements. Young citrus trees should be fed about mid February, May, and August with the final feeding in October. Starting six inches from the trunk of the tree, scatter the fertilizer over the cleared area. Increase the amount to two pounds each feeding for the second and third years. The young trees should be fed a *minimum* of four times each year.

By the fourth year your trees should be treated as bearing trees. Bearing citrus trees should be fed one pound of a quality 6-6-6 or a citrus special for each foot of tree spread. Therefore, a citrus tree with a 10 foot diameter of foliage spread should receive 10 pounds of fertilizer three times each year for a total of 30 pounds of a citrus special each year. They should be fed in February, in May, and a final feeding in October. Scatter the fertilizer evenly over the soil under the tree.

Other fruit trees such as avocado trees will respond well to the fertilizer schedule outlined for citrus.

Nutritional sprays will make your trees more healthy as they feed zinc, manganese, boron, etc. to the tree through their leaves. In most soils these elements are more effectively taken up by the leaves than through the roots.

Nutritional sprays are most effective when applied to the leaves of the spring flush of growth when they are from three-quarters to full grown. Spray thoroughly covering the leaves and twigs.

Use caution in applying iron chelate to young trees as there is danger of severe damage by over dosage.

CITRUS SPRAY PROGRAM

MELANOSE SPRAY—Use a copper spray. Apply it 1 to 3 weeks after most of the petals have fallen. Spray thoroughly covering all fruit, twigs, and leaves. Removal of dead twigs and branches is very beneficial.

GREASY SPOT SPRAY—Use a copper spray about June 15th.

SCALE SPRAY—When scale insects are present, spray with an oil emulsion plus malathion sometime between June 15th and July 15th. Oil emulsions should never be used on trees suffering from drought or late in the fall as late spraying will make them more easily damaged by cold.

MITE SPRAYS—When mites are present, spray with a miticide.

When using any spray read the label carefully and follow all instructions to avoid damage to both the plant and the user.

This spray schedule will work most years. At times it will have to be varied to adapt to the weather and local conditions.

The following are some citrus problems and the way in which they may be controlled.

MANGANESE DEFICIENCY

Manganese deficiency is most noticeable on young leaves and may cause severe leaf drop. This deficiency is prevalent on trees growing in alkaline soil or in soil deficient in manganese.

ZINC DEFICIENCY

Zinc deficiency, Frenching, can cause a loss of fruit production and fruit quality.

Manganese and zinc are most effective when sprayed on the leaves. Most nutritional sprays contain these elements.

IRON DEFICIENCY

Iron deficiency will cause low quality fruit. The leaf pattern is more noticeable on young leaves. Soil application of chelated iron is the only effective way of curing this deficiency in citrus.

MAGNESIUM DEFICIENCY

Magnesium deficiency or bronzing will cause poor yield and poor quality of fruit. This deficiency is quite common and shows up frequently on the older leaves near the maturing fruit. It often causes leaf drop. Magnesium sulphate (Epsom salts) or Emjo is most efficient applied to the soil. Use from ½ to 5 lbs. depending upon the size of the tree.

RUST MITE DAMAGE   SANDPAPER MELANOSE

Rust mites are very small, about 1/200th of an inch long. However, they do much harm to all types of citrus trees, damaging the leaves, twigs, and fruit. Fruit damage is most noticeable. Control rust mites by spraying with a miticide.

Sandpaper melanose is a fungus disease that attacks the fruit, leaves, and twigs. It is most noticeable on grapefruit. Very small, hard, round, mahogany colored lesions are the symptoms. Spraying with copper one to three weeks after most of the petals have fallen usually gives satisfactory control. Careful pruning is also a factor in combating this disease.

Other serious pests of citrus are whiteflies, mealybugs, and red spiders. These are pictured and controls suggested in the book *Florida Insects*.

Some other problems of citrus are pictured and remedies are given in the book *Florida Lawns and Gardens*.

1991 UPDATE ON ADDITIONAL VARIETIES

Page 15. Annona montana is not as palatable but new selections show promise.
Page 18. (Annona cherimola x A. squamosa) Priestly and Lindstrom.
Page 19. Averrhoa carambola Arkin, Maha, Fwang Tung, and Wheeler.
Page 20. Pouteria sapota Copan and Pontin.
Page 24. Casimiroa edulis SES No. 2 and Smathers.
Page 41. Diospyros digyna Joyner, Maher, and Bernecker.
Page 44. Dovyalis abyssinica x hebecarpa. There are several varieties.
Page 46. Eriobotrya japonica Bradenton and Champagne.
Page 49. Eugenia dombeyi. No named varieties yet but some have larger fruit.
Page 56. Garcinia tinctoria is alleged to be a good fruit, but few plants are available.
Page 58. Macadamia integrifolia Beaumont and Heisler.
Page 64. Manilkara zapota Tikal.
Page 77. Pouteria campechiana. Aurea, Bruce, and Ross are good varieties.
Page 84. Psidium guajava Blitch and Ruehle.

WHEN TO PICK YOUR FRUIT
By Al Will, Jr.

How often have you bought fruit at the market and found it to be hard and unripe, tasteless, or bitter? If you're like most of us, it has happened often enough to be annoying. Now that you are growing your own fruit, it is up to YOU to decide on the best time to pick it. In addition to the pride and self-satisfaction that come from growing fruit, you will find that there are other advantages: fuller flavor, because the fruit is picked at its peak; a firm even texture to the flesh; no bruises from shipping or handling; and enough fruit for all your needs, including perhaps canning and supplying your friends with fruit. You may even sell the surplus to a broker or local produce market and find that you have made a profit on your crop.

As for deciding when to pick your fruit, you first must bear in mind the type you are raising. Fruit can be divided into two groups: **normal fruit,** which follows the general ripening and picking pattern; and **unusual fruit,** which for one reason or another follows a different pattern.

Normal fruit may be picked when it reaches a mature size; it can be expected to ripen after picking with good color, the proper texture, and a minimum loss of flavor. These fruits also can be characterized by the uses to which they are put; they can be eaten fresh, canned, or shipped.

When picking fruit to eat fresh, you should always allow it to ripen fully on the plant so that its most delicate flavors are developed and all of its natural vitamins are at their peak. Generally, the "peak of perfection" occurs when the fruit can be picked merely by gripping it lightly and giving it a slight twist. The fruit should fall into your hands. At this point it has developed its full color potential and is usually soft to the touch. (Some exceptions to this— fruit that should be cut from the plant with a knife or shears—are members of the sugar-apple group, pineapple, jak-fruit, bananas, ceriman, and tamarinds.)

Fruit for canning also should be picked when completely ripe, except when making pickled fruit or chutney. For these, the fruit is usually picked when it is fully mature, but not ripe. (Full maturity is the stage of development that just precedes the color change in those fruits that change color. If a ripe fruit is compared to one that is unripe but at full maturity, they should be the same size. Fruit that is to be shipped by mail, or railway express, also should be picked when fully mature but not ripe.

Unusual fruits are those that do not follow the typical ripening pattern. They may be divided into three groups:

1. Some fruits must ripen on the tree because they will not ripen after being picked. Citrus fruits and most citrus relatives, such as the wampi fall into this category; others are Chinese raisin tree, and tamarinds.

2. Some fruits never ripen on the tree, but must be picked when fully mature. For example, the avocado will ripen three to seven days after being picked.

3. Although most fruits do taste better when they are fully ripened on the plant, some fruit taste entirely different when allowed this extra "on the vine" ripening. The final stages of ripening add an extra bit of sugar which improves the taste considerably and removes the slight aftertaste of alum that one sometimes finds. These fruits must never be picked before they are ripe.

KNOW YOUR PLANT FOOD ELEMENTS

PRIMARY PLANT FOOD ELEMENTS

ELEMENT	SYMBOL	SOURCES	DEFICIENCY SYMPTOMS	EXCESS SYMPTOMS	FUNCTION IN PLANT	WHERE FOUND IN PLANT	LEACHING IN SAND	BEST pH RANGE
Nitrogen	N	Organics Synthetics Urea Ammonia Nitrates	Light green to yellow leaves. Stunted growth.	Dark green, soft growth. Retarded maturity. Loss of buds or fruit.	Stimulates growth.	In proteins. In chlorophyll.	Fast.	5.5-7.0 Ammonia may be lost when pH is above 7.0
Phosphorus	P	Superphosphate	Red or purple leaves. Cell division retardation.	Possible tie up of other essential elements.	In enzymes. Hastens maturity. Aids respiration. Required in all cells.	In proteins of the cell nucleus.	Slow.	5.5-7.0
Potash	K	Muriate or Sulphate of Potash	Reduced vigor. Susceptibility to diseases. Thin skin and small fruit.	Coarse, poor colored fruit. Reduced absorption of Mg and Ca.	Translocation of materials in plants. Regulates photosynthesis. Regulates formation of starch.	In the cell sap.	Fast.	5.5-7.0

SECONDARY PLANT FOOD ELEMENTS

ELEMENT	SYMBOL	SOURCES	DEFICIENCY SYMPTOMS	EXCESS SYMPTOMS	FUNCTION IN PLANT	WHERE FOUND IN PLANT	LEACHING IN SAND	BEST pH RANGE
Magnesium	Mg	Magnesium Sulphate (Epsom Salts) Dolomite is 1/3 Mg.	Loss of yield. Chlorosis of old leaves.	Reduced absorption of Ca and K.	Aids photosynthesis. Key element in chlorophyl.	In chlorophyl.	Fast in acid soils. Slower in limed soils.	5.5-6.5
Manganese	Mn	Manganese Sulphate (Tecmangam)	Mottled chlorosis of the leaves. Stunted growth.	Small dead areas in the leaves with yellow borders around them.	In enzyme system.	In enzyme system.	Fast in acid soils. Slower in limed soils.	5.0-5.5
Copper	Cu	Copper Sulphate Neutral Copper	Multiple budding. Gum pockets.	Prevents the uptake of Iron. Causes stunting of roots.	Enzyme activator.	In cell sap.	Slow.	5.5-6.0

MINOR (OR MICRO) ELEMENTS

ELEMENT	SYMBOL	SOURCES	DEFICIENCY SYMPTOMS	EXCESS SYMPTOMS	FUNCTION IN PLANT	WHERE FOUND IN PLANT	LEACHING IN SAND	BEST pH RANGE
Zinc	Zn	Zinc Sulphate	Small, thin, yellow leaves. Low yields.	None known.	Aids in cell division. In enzymes and auxins.	In cell sap.	Slow.	5.0-5.5
Iron	Fe	Iron Sulphate (Copperas) Chelated Iron	Yellowing of leaves, the veins remaining green.	None known.	A catalyst. In the enzyme system. Hemoglobin in legumes.	Part of chlorophyl.	Fast.	5.5-6.0
Sulphur	S	Sulphur Superphosphate	Looks like Nitrogen deficiency.	Sulphur burn from too low pH.	Helps to build proteins.	In proteins and amino acids.	Slow.	5.5-8.0
Calcium	Ca	Lime Basic Slag Gypsum	Stops growing point of plants.	Reduces the intake of K and Mg.	Part of cell walls. Part of enzymes.	In cell walls. (Calcium pectin).	Slow.	5.5-8.0
Molybdenum	Mo	Sodium Molybdate	Hibiscus (strap leaf). Symptoms in plants vary greatly.	Poisonous to livestock.	Helps in the utilization of N.	In enzymes.	Slow.	6.5-8.0
Boron	B	Borax	Small leaves, Heart rot and corkiness. Multiple buds.	Leaves turn yellowish red.	Affects absorption of other elements. Affects germination of pollen tube.	Throughout the plant.	Fast.	5.5-6.5

ELEMENTS FROM AIR AND WATER

ELEMENT	SYMBOL	SOURCES	DEFICIENCY SYMPTOMS	EXCESS SYMPTOMS	FUNCTION IN PLANT	WHERE FOUND IN PLANT
Carbon	C	Air (Carbon Dioxide)	None known.	None known.	Keystone of all organic substances.	In cell walls and in sugars and starches.
Oxygen	O	Air and Water	White areas at leaf veins. High Nitrates.	None known.	Respiration.	Throughout the plant.
Hydrogen	H	Water	Wilting.	Drowning.	Necessary in all plant functions.	A part of sugars and starches.

INCHES

Common Name Velvet-Apple   **Native to** Malaya
                 Mabolo

Habit of Growth Handsome, evergreen tree.   **Florida Height** 25' **Width** 12'

Description Leaves alternate, green above and lighter color, hairy underneath. Male flowers clustered along stem. Female flowers, few, in axils of leaves.

Fruit (Description and Use) Skin dull red to orange, covered with reddish-velvety hairs. Flesh cream colored, soft and mealy. Very aromatic. Pleasant odor of strong cheese.   Eaten fresh.

Flower & Season White, waxy, to 1½"   **Fruit Season** Sept. to Dec.
(female) Summer.

Soil & Moisture Moist, well-drained.   **Freezes about** 29°F.

pH Preference 5.5 to 6.5.   **Sun or Shade** Sun or partial shade.

Rate of Growth Moderate.   **Salt Tolerance** Poor.

Culture Chlorotic on alkaline soils. Spray with nutritional sprays containing essential elements. Mulching is beneficial.

Propagation By seeds. Trees with better fruit can be propagated by air layers, side or veneer grafts.

Problems No serious pests. Trees are damaged by cold winds.

Varieties Seedless forms are known.

40

Scientific Name Diospyros digyna   **Family** Ebenaceae

INCHES

Common Name Black Sapote   **Native to** Mexico
Chocolate Pudding Fruit

Habit of Growth Evergreen, handsome tree.   **Florida Height** 25' **Width** 25'

Description Leaves glossy, dark green, leathery, alternate, with wavy margins. Branches dark brown.

Fruit (Description & Use) Greenish-brown when ripe. Skin thin. Flesh sweet, chocolate-brown in color. Several seeds.   Eaten fresh.

Flower & Season Small and white. May to June.

Fruit Season Nov. to April.

Soil & Moisture Moist, well-drained.

Freezes about 28°F. Young trees 32°F.

pH Preference 5.5 to 7.0.

Sun or Shade Sun or light shade.

Rate of Growth Fast.

Salt Tolerance Fair.

Culture Trees will not take drought conditions.

Propagation Seeds germinate in about 30 days. Seedling tree will fruit in about 5 years.

Problems No serious pests.

Varieties Bell is a known variety.

Scientific Name Diospyros kaki **Family** Ebenaceae

INCHES

TANENASHI

Common Name Oriental Persimmon. **Native to** Asia
Japanese Persimmon.

Habit of Growth Compact deciduous tree **Florida Height** 25' **Width** 20'

Description Leaves dark green above, lighter beneath; texture rough and fairly thick. Tree usually has rounded crown.

Fruit (Description & Use) Skin yellow to red or orange. Fruit to 3" across. Some fruit astringent until fully ripe. Pick and let ripen indoors. Best as fresh fruit.

Flower & Season Yellowish-white, ½" across. Spring. **Fruit Season** Summer and early fall.

Soil & Moisture Moist, well-drained. **Freezes about** 15°F.

pH Preference 5.0 to 6.0. **Sun or Shade** Sun.

Rate of Growth Moderate. **Salt Tolerance** Fair to poor.

Culture Clean cultivation or can be mulched. Most varieties except Tanenashi require cross pollination from the Gailey variety.

Propagation Grafting most common. However, budding from March to September is usually successful—veneer or patch type budding is used.

Problems Scale insects may become a problem. Often a dormant spray with copper to control anthracnose is helpful.
Does not fruit well in extreme southern Florida.

Varieties Refer to the chart on the next page.

42

JAPANESE PERSIMMONS

Persimmons are the near perfect fruit for the Florida home gardener. This delicious fruit is probably the easiest to grow of all our fruit and is being grown in practically every county in Florida. It is usually hardy to cold and can be grown on most soils. (It does not fruit well in extreme southern Florida.)

Only buy grafted varieties. Can grown persimmon trees can be planted at any time of the year.

Although tolerant of dry or wet soils, persimmons like most other plants will do best in a fertile well-drained soil having fair humus content. The tree should be planted in a well prepared planting hole.

Japanese persimmons will do well on a fertilizer program similar to that used on citrus, but persimmons only need about one-half the amount of fertilizer. Nutritional sprays will also be helpful.

The flavor of the non-astringent persimmon is entirely different from the flavor of the astringent kind, such as Tanenashi or Triumph. A thoroughly ripe, juicy, non-astringent persimmon such as Hanafuyu compares favorably in flavor with a good mango.

	Astringency	Color of Skin	Color of Flesh	Flavor	Seeds	Size Length-Diameter	Size	Shape	Tree Vigor	Tree Shape	Fruiting Time
HANAFUYU	Non-Astringent	Reddish-Orange	Somewhat Dark	Excellent Sweet, Juicy	4 or 5	3-3⅛"	Large	Roundish Oblate	Good	Semi-Spreading	Sept.-Oct.
FUYUGAKI	Non-Astringent	Deep Red	Light	Very Sweet	2-4	2½-3¼"	Medium to Large	Short Flattened	Average	Semi-Spreading	Sept.-Oct.
FUYU 72662	Non-Astringent	Deep Red	Light	Medium Sweet	Few	2¼-3"	Medium to Large	Short Flat	Average	Semi-Spreading	Sept.-Oct.
HYAKUME	Non-Astringent	Light Buff to Yellow	Streaked	Sweet Crisp, Meaty	Few	3-3¼"	Large	Roundish Oblong	Good Bears Well	Shape Varies	Oct.
OGASHA	Non-Astringent	Orange-Red	Medium Dark	Sweet Crisp	3	2¾-3½"	Large Tapers	Flattened, Blunt point at apex	Fair	Open Spreading	Late Sept.-Oct.
TANENASHI	Astringent	Light Yellow to Bright Red	Yellow	Very Good	None	3½-2¾"	Large to Very Large	Roundish Conical	Prolific	Rounded	Sept.-Oct.
TAMOPAN	Astringent	Reddish-Orange	Light Yellow, Soft	Good	None	3-5"	Medium to Large	Constriction around fruit	Vigorous Prolific, Hungry	Tall and Willowy	Oct.-Nov.
TRIUMPH	Astringent	Bright Red	Clear Orange	Good	Several	1¾-2¼"	Small	Flatish	Good for South Florida	Upright	Oct.-Nov.
GAILEY	Astringent	Dull Red	Dark	Poor, Used for pollination	Many	2-1¾"	Small	Rounded	Good-Fair	Semi-Spreading	Oct.-Nov.

Scientific Name Dovyalis abyssinica x hebecarpa   **Family** Flacourtiaceae

INCHES

Common Name Tropical Apricot.   **Native to** Natural hybrid in Florida

Habit of Growth Large, spreading shrub.   **Florida Height** 15′ **Width** 15′

Description Leaves 3″ to 4″ long, pale green. Branches long and drooping. Plants vary greatly as to number and size of thorns.

Fruit (Description & Use) Skin velvety, brownish yellow in color, to 1¼″ across. Flesh soft, melting, apricot flavor.   Eaten fresh, in jellies or drink.

Flower & Season Small greenish-yellow. Sept.-Jan.

Fruit Season Dec.-April.

Soil & Moisture Rich, moist soil.

Freezes about 26°F.

pH Preference 5.5 to 6.5.

Sun or Shade Sun or partial shade.

Rate of Growth Fast.

Salt Tolerance Poor.

Culture Fruit needs to be thinned to produce larger fruit. An isolated tree will produce fruit.

Propagation From cuttings or air layers. When grafted on D. hebecarpa it seems to be less thorny and produces more fruit.

Problems No serious pests.

Varieties There are two varieties—ask for "sweet" variety.

44

INCHES

Common Name Kei-Apple   **Native to** South Africa

Habit of Growth Dense, thorny shrub.   **Florida Height** 15′ **Width** 10′

Description Leaves shiny green. Has one large stiff spine to each node. Leaves in clusters at nodes. Twigs wiry.

Fruit (Description & Use) Skin clear yellow when ripe. Contains 5 or more flattened pointed seeds. Flavor suggests apricot.
Sometimes eaten fresh, in preserves and jelly.

Flower & Season Small, yellowish (dioecious) Feb.-June.

Fruit Season May-Sept.

Soil & Moisture Tolerant.

Freezes about 22°F. Recovers quickly.

pH Preference 5.5 to 7.5.

Sun or Shade Sun.

Rate of Growth Slow.

Salt Tolerance Fair back from beach.

Culture Must have male and female plants for fruit.
Will withstand drought. They make an impenetrable hedge.

Propagation By seeds, cutting, or by budding.

Problems No serious pests. Juice of fruit stains clothing.

Varieties No superior varieties known.

INCHES

Common Name Loquat   **Native to** China
                   Japanese Plum
Habit of Growth Small, well-shaped tree.   **Florida Height** 25' **Width** 20'
Description Leaves large to 12" long, stiff. Dark green above and whitish
   underneath. Margins toothed.
Fruit (Description & Use) Color yellow to orange, usually pear-shaped, smooth
   to 1½" across and 2" long with 3 to 5 seeds.   Eaten fresh or as jelly

Flower & Season Whitish, terminal,   **Fruit Season** Jan. to April. (Summer
   fragrant. Oct.-Feb.   blooms produce no fruit.)

                                               Freezes about 12°F. (Flowers and
Soil & Moisture Rich, moist soil.   fruit 27°F.)

pH Preference 5.5 to 7.5.   **Sun or Shade** Sun.

                                               Salt Tolerance Very good, used in
Rate of Growth Moderate.   beach plantings.

Culture Trees that are well fed and watered bear larger fruit. Thin fruit to
   increase size. Flavor of fruit varies greatly. Seedling trees usually bear small,
   poor fruit.
Propagation Grafts of selected varieties. Fruit from improved varieties are some
   of Florida's finest fruit.
Problems Fire blight, to control prune and destroy clippings. Then spray with
   neutral copper 3 times at 2 week intervals. Aphids.
Varieties Fletcher, Oliver, Premier, Wolfe, Thales, Gold Nugget, Olivier.

LOQUATS

The loquat or Japanese plum is a beautiful small tree for both shade and fruit. It will grow on a variety of soils and is rather salt tolerant. Although it will grow under unsatisfactory conditions, to produce good crops of large fruit it must be well fertilized and have ample moisture. However, it will not stand "wet feet." (Thinning of the fruit will increase the size of the remaining fruit.) Be sure and plant your grafted tree in a well prepared planting hole.

Loquats will do well with the citrus fertilization program.

FIRE BLIGHT

Loquat trees have one serious disease. It is fire blight which is caused by the bacterium Erwinia amylovora. This disease causes death of twigs, branches, and occasionally the entire tree. Fire blight can usually be controlled by prompt removal and burning of diseased parts. The tree should then be sprayed with neutral copper three times at two week intervals.

	TREE GROWTH	RIPENING DATE (Approx.)	FRUIT COLOR	FRUIT SIZE		QUALITY FLAVOR
				DIAMETER	LENGTH	
Advance	Good	March 30	Whitish	1½"	2⅛"	Good
Bartow or Fletcher White	Good	April 5	Whitish	1½"	1¾"	Good
Bradenton or Hastings	Vigorous	April 1	Pale Yellow	1½"	2"	Excellent
Fletcher Red	Upright Weak	March 25	Orange-Red	1½"	2⅛"	Excellent Keeps well
Gold Nugget	Vigorous Very ornamental	February 21	Yellow	1¼"	1½"	Fair to Good
Hardee	Vigorous	April 1	Pale Yellow	1½" +	1⅝"	Fair
*Oliver	Vigorous	April 1	Deep Yellow	1½"	1½"	Excellent
Premier	Slow	February 21	Pale Yellow	1"	1½"	Excellent Sweetest
SES 2	Vigorous	March 30	Pale Yellow	1⅜"	1¾"	Good
Thales	Vigorous	April 8	Yellow	1⅜"	1½"	Good
Wolfe	Vigorous	April 1	Pale Yellow	1¼"	1¾"	Fair. Excellent for cooking

*Oliver   (from Glen St. Mary's Nursery)

INCHES

Common Name Cherry of the Rio Grande   **Native to** Brazil

Habit of Growth Small, evergreen tree.   **Florida Height** 15′ **Width** 5′

Description Leaves opposite, dark green and glossy. Petioles grooved. Bark peels on trunk leaving trunk smooth.

Fruit (Description & Use) Dark red, to 1″, oblong. Persistent calyx. Skin thin. Pulp juicy, usually one seed.   Eaten fresh or in jelly and jam.

Flower & Season White, solitary March to May.

Fruit Season April-June.

Soil & Moisture Good, moist soil.

Freezes about 20°F. (Twigs damaged.)

pH Preference 5.5 to 6.5.

Sun or Shade Sun.

Rate of Growth Slow.

Salt Tolerance Fair.

Culture Should be well fed and watered. Takes about 10 years to bear from seed.

Propagation Now raised from seed. Grafts and air layers difficult due to hard wood. Mist propagation may be feasible.

Problems Slight dieback a problem. No known control.

Varieties No improved types known.

Scientific Name Eugenia dombeyi   **Family** Myrtaceae

INCHES

Common Name Grumichama   **Native to** Brazil

Habit of Growth Small, compact tree.   **Florida Height** 15' **Width** 10'

Description Leaves leathery, opposite, beautiful glossy green, 3" to 4" long and 1" to 2" wide. Young growth reddish.

Fruit (Description & Use) Fruit on long stems, purplish-black, often in small clusters. It has large persistent sepals. Flesh white, melting, and tasty. Very good fresh, also in jelly or stewed.

Flower & Season White to 1", in leaf axil. Mainly from March to April.

Fruit Season April to June. Takes only one month from flower to fruit.

Soil & Moisture Acid, rich, moist.

Freezes about 27°F. (Tops froze)

pH Preference 5.5 to 6.5.

Sun or Shade Sun or partial shade.

Salt Tolerance Fair. Chlorotic on beach sands.

Rate of Growth Moderate.

Culture Suffers from drought. Use of minor elements is desirable.

Propagation Seeds germinate in about a month. Superior types are grafted.

Problems No serious pests. Use nutritional spray on spring flush of growth.

Varieties No named varieties yet.

49

INCHES

Common Name Pitomba   **Native to** Brazil

Habit of Growth Spreading, evergreen tree.   **Florida Height** 15' **Width** 10'

Description Leaves narrow, opposite, leathery, dense. Glossy deep green above, light green beneath. Trunk mottled brown and tan.

Fruit (Description & Use) Showy bright yellow, to 1½" across. Skin thin, has persistent calyx. Soft, melting, sweet to sub-acid, aromatic. Good as fresh fruit.

Flower & Season Showy white to 1" across. April- June.

Fruit Season May-July. Sometimes a light fall crop.

Soil & Moisture Needs moisture.

Freezes about 27°F.

pH Preference 5.5 to 7.5.

Sun or Shade Sun.

Rate of Growth Moderate.

Salt Tolerance Good if well fed.

Culture An easy to grow tree that responds well to fertilizer, minor elements, and good soil moisture. Use nutritional spray on spring flush of growth.

Propagation By seeds. Grafted plants superior but rarely available.

Problems No serious pests.

Varieties None known.

Scientific Name Eugenia uniflora   **Family** Myrtaceae

INCHES

Common Name Surinam-Cherry   **Native to** Brazil
Pitanga

Habit of Growth Compact, ornamental shrub.   **Florida Height** 15′   **Width** 15′

Description Leaves, waxy, glossy to 2″ long. Leaves deep red when young. Can be pruned to a small tree to 15′, or used as a shrub or a hedge plant.

Fruit (Description & Use) Dark red or black when ripe. About 1″ in diameter. 8 ribbed. Fruit much better on some clones.   Eaten fresh or in jellies.

Flower & Season Creamy-white ½″ across. April-May.

Fruit Season May-June. May fruit most of year.

Soil & Moisture Very tolerant.

Freezes about 30°F. Will come back.

pH Preference 5.5 to 7.5.

Sun or Shade Sun.

Rate of Growth Moderate.

Salt Tolerance Fair when well fed.

Culture Well fed and watered plants have better and larger fruit.

Propagation By seed that will germinate in 3-4 weeks. Better fruited varieties may be side grafted. Root cuttings are sometimes used.

Problems No serious pests except Caribbean fruit fly.

Varieties Varieties with better fruit are available.

51

Scientific Name Euphoria longana   **Family** Sapindaceae

INCHES

Common Name Longan   **Native to** India

Habit of Growth Large, symmetrical tree.   **Florida Height** 40′ **Width** 45′

Description Leaves alternate, compound, glossy to 12″ long. Leaflets alternate or nearly opposite. Leaflets dark green, leathery. Twigs brown and wooly.

Fruit (Description & Use) On spikes, rusty-reddish to an inch across. Layer of pulp around seed has good flavor.   Fresh fruit.

Flower & Season Small on upright panicles. Jan.-Feb.

Fruit Season July-Aug.

Soil & Moisture Good, moist soil.

Freezes about 24°F.

pH Preference 5.5 to 7.0.

Sun or Shade Sun.

Rate of Growth Slow.

Salt Tolerance Poor.

Culture Tree hardier and easier to grow than lychee. Mulching helpful. Needs minor elements. Tree wind resistant.

Propagation Air layers or by grafting. Seedlings slow & uncertain and take 10 to 20 years to bear.

Problems No serious pests. Scale insects.

Varieties Kohala. There is a great variation in seedling fruit size and flavor.

52

Scientific Name Feijoa sellowiana   **Family** Myrtaceae

INCHES

Common Name Feijoa
          Pineapple-Guava

Native to South America

Habit of Growth Rounded dense shrub.

Florida Height 15' **Width** 15'

Description Leaves stiff, shiny green above, light grayish-green underneath. Bark gray.

Fruit (Description & Use) Gray-green in color. Ripe fruit rarely found on bush in Florida. It usually drops. Pick when mature, take indoors to ripen.
          Eaten fresh or in jelly.

Flower & Season Thick white petals scarlet stamens. Petals edible. Apr.-May.

Fruit Season Aug.-Oct.

Soil & Moisture Most soils.

Freezes about 14°F. Hardy.

pH Preference 5.5 to 7.0

Sun or Shade Sun.

Rate of Growth Slow.

Salt Tolerance Very Good.

Culture The cooler the growing season the better the fruit. Feijoas bear better when various clones are planted together. An excellent ornamental shrub.

Propagation Usually from seeds which germinate in 2 to 3 weeks. Superior varieties are grafted.

Problems No serious pests. Rarely sets fruit in lower S. E. Florida.

Varieties Choiceana, Superba, Coolidge, Triumph, and Mammoth. Plant at least three varieties for proper cross pollination.

53

Scientific Name Ficus carica   **Family** Moraceae

INCHES

Common Name Fig   **Native to** Asia Minor

Habit of Growth Low, spreading tree.   **Florida Height** 12′ **Width** 12′

Description Leaves large, lobed, palmately veined, to 8″. Rough above with fine hairs underneath. Deciduous.

Fruit (Description & Use) Pear-shaped, hollow, fleshy, 1″ to 3″, green, yellow, pink, violet, brown, and black.   Fresh fruit or preserves.

Flower & Season Flower within fruit. Early summer to fall.

Fruit Season Early summer to fall.

Soil & Moisture Tolerant, will withstand poor drainage.

Freezes about 7°F. if dormant. Young growth is very tender.

pH Preference 5.5 to 8.0.

Sun or Shade Sun.

Rate of Growth Rapid.

Salt Tolerance Poor.

Culture Keep mulched. Responds to good care and fertilization.

Propagation Graft on Ficus glomerata or F. gnaphthlacarpa for nematode resistance. Cuttings from 2 to 3 year old wood.

Problems Birds and fig rust.

Varieties Celeste, Brown Turkey, Brunswick (Magnolia), Black Mission, and Green Ischia.

Scientific Name Flacourtia indica   **Family** Flacourtiaceae

INCHES

Common Name Governors-Plum   **Native to** Madagascar, S. Asia
Ramontchi

Habit of Growth Dense, rounded shrub.   **Florida Height** 15' **Width** 15'

Description Leaves leathery, glossy, deep green above, pale green underneath. Some have sharp spines.

Fruit (Description & Use) Dark red to almost purple, ¾" to 1" across. Flesh soft with several small seeds.   Eaten fresh, fair flavor, in jams and jellies.

Flower & Season Small, in leaf axils. April-July.

Fruit Season June-Oct.

Soil & Moisture Sand or limestone.

Freezes about 26°F.

pH Preference 6.0 to 8.0.

Sun or Shade Sun.

Rate of Growth Moderate to rapid.

Salt Tolerance Fair.

Culture Prune to keep in bounds. Does well even if neglected. A good hedge plant. Some plants male; some female, some bisexual.

Propagation Seeds, suckers, cuttings of mature wood, or by grafting.

Problems No serious pests.

Varieties A good bisexual variety is available in some nurseries.

INCHES

Common Name Imbe   **Native to** Portuguese E. Africa

Habit of Growth Small tree, unusual form.   **Florida Height** 10' **Width** variable

Description Leaves oblong, leathery, 4" to 6" long, dark green with white veins. Tree limbs have unique weird form.

Fruit (Description & Use) Dull orange to yellow, 1½" to 2" across. Has thin skin and one seed surrounded by a thin watery pulp of pleasing flavor.
Eaten fresh.

Flower & Season Greenish-yellow in clusters. Trees dioecious. April-May.

Soil & Moisture Tolerant of drought.

pH Preference 5.5 to 7.5.

Rate of Growth Moderate.

Fruit Season July-August.

Freezes about 26°F.

Sun or Shade Full sun or light shade.

Salt Tolerance Good.

Culture Will grow on limestone soils. Blooms twice some seasons.

Propagation By seed, no selected clones.

Problems Use zinc spray. Pulp and juice of fruit stain clothing.

Varieties G. mangostana, which will not grow here, is known as "King of Fruits." G. tinctoria is alleged to be a good fruit, but no plants are available.

Scientific Name Litchi chinensis   **Family** Sapindaceae

INCHES

Common Name Lychee   **Native to** S. E. China.

Habit of Growth Round-headed tree.   **Florida Height** 35' **Width** 35'

Description Leaves compound, alternate, pinnate, with 2 to 4 pairs of leathery, shining leaflets. New growth coppery-red.

Fruit (Description & Use) Round to ovate, to 1½" in diameter, in clusters. Skin a thin leathery shell, purplish-red to bright red when ripe. Flesh white and juicy with excellent flavor and aroma.   Eaten fresh. Freezes well.

Flower & Season Small yellowish clusters. Jan. Feb.

Soil & Moisture Acid, moist soil.

pH Preference 5.5 to 7.0.

Rate of Growth Moderate.

Fruit Season Mid June-Mid July.

Freezes about 26°F. Young trees tender.

Sun or Shade Sun.

Salt Tolerance Poor.

Culture Young trees should be protected from wind. Trees require good moisture when fruiting. Should be heavily mulched and given nutritional spray in spring.

Propagation Plants from air layering off selected trees can fruit in 2 years. Grafting except for inarching and approach grafting usually unsuccessful.

Problems Spray for lychee bark scale and spider mites when present. Mushroom root rot can be a serious problem.

Varieties Brewster, Mauritius, Sweet Cliff, Bengal, Kwai Mi, Hak Ip, No Mai, Hanging Green, Yellow Red, Calcutta, Groff, Grove Special, Amboina, Annie Wong, Peerless, and others.

Scientific Name Macadamia integrifolia   **Family** Proteaceae

Common Name Macadamia   **Native to** Australia (Queensland)
Queensland Nut

Habit of Growth Tree of variable shape.   **Florida Height** 25' **Width** 20'

Description Leaves dark green often with prickly edges, to 8" long and 2" wide. In whorls of 3.

Fruit (Description & Use) Nut with very hard shell, ½" to 1" in diameter. Husk glossy and smooth, splits open.   Delicious fresh nut, roasted or salted.

Flower & Season Small white, no petals, in racemes. Spring.

Fruit Season Nov.-March.
(6 to 7 months from flower to nut)

Soil & Moisture Rich, deep soil.

pH Preference 5.5 to 6.5.

Freezes about 24°F.

Rate of Growth Moderate (young). Slow (older).

Sun or Shade Sun.

Salt Tolerance Poor.

Culture Will stand some flooding and will stand some drought when established. Nuts can be stored after drying for several months.

Propagation By seeds or marcottage. Buy superior marcotted varieties. From seed to fruiting 10-12 years. By marcottage will bear in 5 to 6 years.

Problems No serious pests.

Varieties Macadamia tetraphylla has spiny edged leaves in whorls of 4.

58

Scientific Name Malpighia punicifolia   **Family** Malpighiaceae
           M. glabra

INCHES

Common Name Barbados-Cherry   **Native to** West Indies __
           Acerola   Central America

Habit of Growth Densely branched shrub.   **Florida Height** 12′ **Width** 10′

Description Leaves deep shiny green, varying in size and shape.

Fruit (Description & Use) About 1″ across, bright red when ripe. Slightly 3 lobed. Thin skinned. Flesh yellow-orange. Very high in Vitamin C.
                                       Eaten fresh or frozen.

Flower & Season Pink to rose. Five   **Fruit Season** May-Nov.
petals. April-Oct.   Sparsely most of the year.

Soil & Moisture Rich, well-drained.   **Freezes about** 30°F.

pH Preference 5.5 to 6.5.   **Sun or Shade** Sun or semishade.

Rate of Growth Moderate.   **Salt Tolerance** Fair.

Culture Should be heavily mulched (nematodes). Keep well watered when in flower or fruit. Use nutritional sprays.

Propagation By hardwood cuttings or marcottage. Can be grafted. Seedlings have poor, sour fruit.

Problems Nematodes serious. Whiteflies, plant bugs, and scale insects. Young shrubs are very tender.

Varieties Buy only improved clones such as Florida Sweet or B-17.

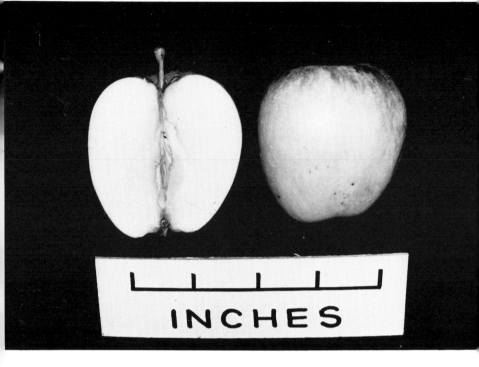

INCHES

Common Name Anna Apple   **Native to** West Asia

Habit of Growth Upright tree.   **Florida Height** 15-18' **Width** 10-12'

Description Tree size will depend on vigor and age with a 15 to 20 year old tree expected to be above height and width. Life span unknown but probably 40 to 50 years or more.

Fruit (Description & Use) 50% red overcolor, Delicious shape, 2½" diameter, sweet, sub-acid, medium firm flesh. Keeps 4 to 6 weeks in refrigerator.
Good for eating fresh or pastries. Freezes well for pastries.

Flower & Season Pink, abundant ornamental in late February to mid March. Rarely has frost damage to flowers.

Fruit Season Late May to mid June. Fruit ripening during rainy season subject to bitter rot.

Soil & Moisture Well-drained. Water needed in dry seasons.

Freezes about Hardy in Florida.

pH Preference 6.0-6.5.

Sun or Shade Full sun—will tolerate light shade.

Rate of Growth Rapid under good conditions.

Salt Tolerance Unknown.

Culture Does poorly in wet soils. Responds well to irrigation in dry season in well-drained soils. It is usually deficient in boron and zinc.

Propagation Grafted or budded on seedling stock. Dwarfing stocks are not adapted to S. E. United States.

Problems Fire blight and bitter rot. 2% dormant oil spray for scale (San Jose). Does not fruit well in south Florida.

Varieties Pollinators: Dorsett Golden and Ein Shemer. Cross pollination is required.

Scientific Name Mangifera indica   **Family** Anacardiaceae

INCHES

Common Name Mango   **Native to** N. India, Burma, Malaya

Habit of Growth Large, variable tree.   **Florida Height 50' Width 40'**

Description Leaves long, pointed. Petiole 1" to 4" long, swollen at the base.

Fruit (Description & Use) Vary in size and shape. Colors green, yellow, orange, red, and purple. Flesh pale yellow to orange. Flavor of most luscious, peachlike.   Fresh fruit, freezes well.

Flower & Season Small, terminal in large clusters. Late Dec.-mid Feb.

Soil & Moisture Well-drained, sandy soil.

pH Preference 5.5 to 7.0.

Rate of Growth Moderate.

Fruit Season May to October.

Freezes about 30°F. Young trees tender.

Sun or Shade Sun.

Salt Tolerance Fairly good.

Culture Young trees can use the regular citrus fertilization program. For older (bearing) trees see article on mangoes. Zinc and manganese nutritional sprays helpful.

Propagation Seedlings not recommended as fruit flavor is variable. Plants by veneer grafting and chip budding of superior varieties are best.

Problems Spray to prevent anthracnose as outlined in mango article. Scale insects, red spiders, and thrips.

Varieties See article on mangoes.

MANGOES

Mangoes are a tropical fruit. They do well in the warmer areas of Florida or in protected areas.

The worst insect pests of mango trees are mango shield scale, pyriform scale and Florida red scale. Use Malathion to control these pests. It usually takes more than one spraying.

At times red-banded thrips will attack the leaves and fruit. Their feeding stain the leaves a dark rusty color.

Spider mites, or red spiders, are frequently seen feeding on the upper surface of the leaves. The feeding of these mites causes the leaves to turn brown and to drop. Sulphur will control these mites.

If powdery mildew occurs use a sulphur spray.

RIPE ROT — ANTHRACNOSE ON MANGO

Anthracnose is the primary fungus disease of mango leaves and fruit. It is a leaf spot disease on the leaf, and it causes round rotten areas on the fruit (ripe rot) and tear staining. At times, small fruit are killed and then mummify on the trees.

ANTHRACNOSE ON MANGO LEAF

Anthracnose lives on both living leaves and twigs and also on dead twigs. Pruning is helpful. A fungicidal spray program to prevent anthracnose on the fruit is necessary.

SPRAY PROGRAM FOR ANTHRACNOSE PREVENTION ON MANGO FRUIT

1. Spray trees thoroughly each week from first appearance of blooms until all fruit are about the size of a pea.
Use a neutral copper or Benlate spray at the strength recommended on the label.

2. Then spray each month until fruit are harvested.

3. These sprays will also help to control mango scab.

Nutritional sprays will help to control zinc and manganese deficiencies. Do not include nitrogen in these sprays.

Nitrogen levels that are suitable for foliage growth can be much too high for good fruit quality, especially for late varieties.

Therefore, bearing trees should be fertilized with a medium level nitrogen fertilizer containing minor elements once a year — in late August or early September, after harvest.

The most important factor affecting fruit flavor after variety are nitrogen levels and stage of ripeness. Try eating mangoes at different stages of ripeness. Some varieties are better while they are still partly green, a few need to be very ripe while most are better somewhere in between.

VARIETY	TIME WHEN RIPE	COLOR WHEN RIPE	FIBER	SKIN THICKNESS	SIZE IN POUNDS	TREE SIZE	RATE OF GROWTH	FOLIAGE	FRUIT PRODUCTION
Carrie	June-July	Yellow	None	Thin	¾-1	Large Spreading	Moderate	Very Dense	Moderately Heavy
Keitt	Aug.-Oct.	Pink, Yellow	Very Little	Medium	1-4	Large	Moderate	Open	Heavy
Julie	June-July	Pink, Yellow	None	Medium	¾-1	Dwarf	Extremely Slow	Dense	Moderate
Kent	July-Sept.	Pink, Yellow Red	None	Thick	1-2½	Medium	Moderate	Very Dense	Moderately Heavy
Beverly	July-Oct.	Yellow	None	Medium	¾-1½	Medium	Moderate	Dense	Heavy
Edward	May-July	Pale Pink Yellow	None	Medium	¾-1	Medium	Moderate	Dense	Moderate
Glenn	May-July	Pink, Yellow	None	Thin	¾-1	Medium	Moderate	Dense	Heavy
Valencia Pride	June-July	Pink, Yellow	None	Medium	¾-2	Large Upright	Very Fast	Dense	Moderate
Philippine	May-July	Yellow	None	Thin	½-¾	Large	Fast	Dense	Heavy but Alternate
Nam Doc Mai	July-Aug.	Yellow	None	Thin	¾-1½	Small	Slow	Dense	Moderate

Carrie, Keitt, and Philippine are resistant to anthracnose.

Chart courtesy of Zill High Performance Plants, Boynton Beach.

Scientific Name Manilkara zapota
(Achras sapota)

Family Sapotaceae

INCHES

Common Name Sapodilla

Native to Tropical America

Habit of Growth Dense, beautiful tree.

Florida Height 40' **Width** 30'

Description Leaves thick, glossy green, clustered at tips of twigs. Wood hard and termite resistant. Milky sap when boiled down is original "chicle" chewing gum.

Fruit (Description and Use) Globose to ovoid. 2" to 4" in diameter. Grayish brown. Fruit have large black seeds. Very prolific. Eaten fresh and in sherbets.

Flower & Season Inconspicuous, white, in leaf axils. Nov.-Feb.

Fruit Season May-Aug. Some all year.

Freezes about 28°F. Young trees 30°F.

Soil & Moisture Tolerant of most soils.

pH Preference 6.0 to 8.0.

Sun or Shade Sun.

Rate of Growth Slow.

Salt Tolerance Good.

Culture Grows well with a minimum of care. A clean tree, quite wind resistant.

Propagation From seed 8 to 9 years to fruit. Superior varieties are grafted or air layered. (Air layering slow 5 to 6 months, but will fruit in 4 to 5 years).

Problems Scale insects.

Varieties Prolific, Russell, Brown Sugar, Seedless, and Modella are superior types.

Scientific Name Muntingia calabura   **Family** Tiliaceae

INCHES

Common Name Strawberry-Tree
Capulin

Native to Trop. America & W. Indies

Habit of Growth Fast growing, sparse tree.   **Florida Height** 20' **Width** 15'

Description Leaves 3" to 5" long with toothed edges. Lower surface of leaf hairy and gray in color. Limbs brittle.

Fruit (Description & Use) Round to ½" across, bright red, and smooth. Very sweet, juicy pulp with many minute (edible) seeds.

Eaten fresh or in jams or tarts

Flower & Season White, strawberry-like. Mostly April-Oct.

Fruit Season All year on mature trees.

Soil & Moisture Rich, moist soil.

Freezes about 28°F.

pH Preference 5.5 to 6.5.

Sun or Shade Sun.

Rate of Growth Rapid.

Salt Tolerance Poor.

Culture Needs pruning to prevent wind damage and to increase fruiting. Normally a short-lived tree.

Propagation Fruits 2nd year from seed. Air layers may fruit the first year.

Problems No serious pests.

Varieties White and yellow fruited forms known, but not available.

65

Scientific Name Musa hybrid   **Family** Musaceae

Common Name Banana   **Native to** India, China

Habit of Growth Large, herbaceous plant.   **Florida Height** 5' to 25' **Width—**

Description Leaves large; the trunk is composed of leaf bases. Suckers at base of plant from underground stems or corms.

Fruit (Description & Use) Bananas of various sizes and shapes. Seedless. Bananas used as fresh fruit. Plantains are cooked.

Flower & Season Large drooping. Plants flower when 12-18 months old.

Fruit Season Varies. Takes 3 months from flower to fruit.

Soil & Moisture Rich, good moisture.

Freezes about 28° F. Leaves 30°F.

pH Preference 5.5 to 6.5.

Sun or Shade Sun.

Rate of Growth Rapid when fertilized.

Salt Tolerance Poor.

Culture Requires two frost free years to fruit. Must have organic fertilizer. Needs well-drained soil but enough water. Easily damaged by wind. Cut down and remove stem after fruiting.

Propagation From suckers. Select thick stemmed suckers. Let dry out a day before planting. Thin to 3 or 4 replacement suckers per plant.

Problems Cold and starvation as they are seldom fed enough.

Varieties See article on bananas.

66

BANANAS
By Eric V. Golby

Bananas appreciate being planted in a moist part of the garden where the soil is rich. They should be heavily fertilized (once a month) during warm weather. The banana clump should be mulched with decayable organic matter.

Each clump should consist of a fruiting stalk and three to four suckers of varying sizes. Thinning to three suckers ensures larger fruit and more continuous fruiting.

After the plant has flowered and all the banana hands are formed, the long "tail" of useless male flowers should be cut off about six inches below the last hand. This removes useless weight and tissue which would sap the plant and enables the plant to produce larger bananas. Care should be taken when doing this as the sap from the stem will make an indelible stain on clothes.

Banana plants can be grown throughout the State. However, in the northern areas the plants are frozen down each year and, therefore, never produce much mature fruit.

VARIETIES

Cavendish banana, a dwarf type, is probably the best adapted to Florida conditions. It grows to a height of 5 to 7 feet. The fruit is medium sized, thin skinned, and of good quality. The Cavendish plant is slightly more cold hardy than others. Also, the leaves are thicker and more wind resistant.

The Apple banana, Manzana, is a tall, thin plant that grows to a height of about 18 feet. It produces short, fat bananas. When picked from the plant when fully sized and then aged for a short time, they are the finest eating bananas of all. The Apple banana, which often has leaf petioles tinged with red, will grow and produce fruit with moderate care.

The Lady-Finger banana is smaller, has thin skinned fruit, and the flavor is milder than the Manzana.

Red Jamaica banana has leaves that are a reddish, bronzy-green. The fruit are large, fat, and stubby with a bronzy-pink skin. The flesh is drier, and the plant is tender to cold. It is a beautiful plant.

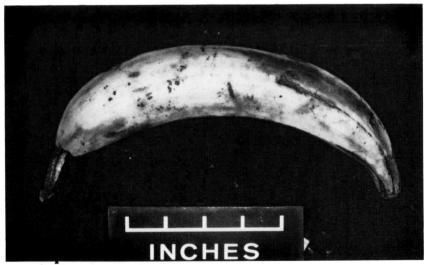

PLANTAINS

There are several varieties of plantains grown in Florida.

The Horse banana or Orinoco is the hardiest and is used primarily as a landscape plant to give a tropical look to the home.

Plantains are usually cooked, baked, or fried.

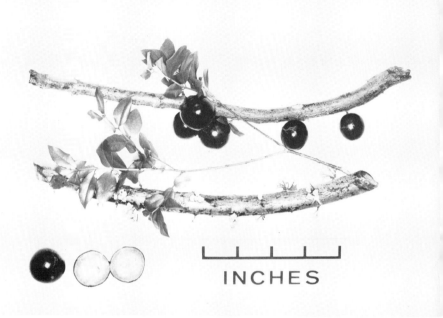

INCHES

Common Name Jaboticaba.   **Native to** Brazil

Habit of Growth Small, bushy tree.   **Florida Height** 15' **Width** 10'

Description Leaves opposite, lanceolate, under 2" long and ¾" wide. Bark peels much like guava bark. Twigs small. Evergreen.

Fruit (Description & Use) Grapelike with tough purple skin to 1" diameter. Pleasant grapelike flavor. Pulp juicy with few small seeds.
Eaten as fresh fruit, in jams and wine. Freezes well.

Flower & Season Small, white, on branches and trunk. Spring to Fall.

Fruit Season May have 5 or 6 crops a year. Takes 1 month from flower to fruit.

Soil & Moisture Rich soil.

Freezes about 24°F. Often stands more.

pH Preference 5.5 to 6.5.

Sun or Shade Sun.

Rate of Growth Slow.

Salt Tolerance None.

Culture Plant in soil fortified with lots of organic matter — peat, manure, etc. Protect from strong winds. Girdling will shock plant into blooming.

Propagation By seeds that sprout in about a month; then 10 years to bear fruit. Air layers with difficulty. Very slow to graft. Air layers may fruit in 4-6 years.

Problems Deficient in essential elements; use nutritional sprays and keep mulched. Needs added iron for good growth.

Varieties No named varieties available in Florida.

Scientific Name Opuntia ficus-indica   **Family** Cactaceae

INCHES

Common Name Prickly-Pear   **Native to** Undetermined.
                  Indian-Fig

Habit of Growth Zigzag pattern.   **Florida Height** 7' **Width** 7'

Description Thick, green, fleshy pads with bluish bloom. Spines usually absent; occasionally 1 to 2 weak spines present on pad.

Fruit (Description & Use) Pear-shaped, yellow, 3" or more long. Pulp red, juicy, slightly tart but pleasant and refreshing. Many fine seeds. Cut out areas with little spines.   Eaten fresh.

Flower & Season Yellowish, about 3"   **Fruit Season** Aug.-Sept.
across. June and July.

Soil & Moisture Stands drought.   **Freezes about** 26°F.

pH Preference 6.0 to 8.5.   **Sun or Shade** Sun.

Rate of Growth Moderate.   **Salt Tolerance** Good.

Culture Best planted in open sunny area. Handle with leather gloves or burlap.

Propagation Break or cut off pads. Let end dry and plant next day with about 1 inch of pad in ground where it is to grow.

Problems Root-knot nematodes. Scale insects. Fungus diseases when humidity is high. Does not do well in humid southern Florida.

Varieties None known.

70

Scientific Name Passiflora edulis   **Family** Passifloraceae

INCHES

Common Name Passion-Fruit   **Native to** Brazil

Habit of Growth Rampant, woody vine.   **Florida Height** Vine **Width—**

Description Leaves 3-lobed, serrate. Vine perennial, climbs with tendrils.
Requires strong support.

Fruit (Description & Use) Slightly oval, purple, shell-like rind. Pulp juicy and
aromatic, containing many seeds.   Eaten fresh or as a juice or in fruit salads.

Flower & Season Purple and white.   **Fruit Season** Summer to midwinter.
Heaviest spring and summer.

Soil & Moisture Good, moist soil.   **Freezes about** 30°F.

pH Preference 5.5 to 7.0.   **Sun or Shade** Sun.

Rate of Growth Rapid.   **Salt Tolerance** Poor.

Culture Grow on strong arbor or fence. Keep well mulched. More should be
planted every 3rd year in new soil.

Propagation Seeds germinate in from 2 weeks to 3 months. Plants from seeds may
fruit within one year. Most plants are self sterile. By having several seedling
plants, proper pollination can occur.

Problems Nematodes, caterpillars, and crown rot. Poor pollination. Best pollinators
are leaf-cutter bees which are scarce in some areas.

Varieties P. edulis var. flavicarpa (pictured) is vigorous and productive. Has yellow
fruit. P. quadrangularis grows well in south Florida.

INCHES

Common Name Avocado   **Native to** Tropical America

Habit of Growth Large, evergreen tree.   **Florida Height** 20'-60' **Width** 25'-35'

Description Leaves large, leathery, from 4" to 8" long. Tips pointed.

Fruit (Description & Use) Round to pear-shaped. Weight varies from a few ounces to a few pounds. Pulp when ripe is of a buttery consistency.
Fruit is best in salads.

Flower & Season Yellowish-green, ½" across. Jan.-April.   **Fruit Season** Different varieties ensure fruit nearly all year.

Soil & Moisture Well-drained soil (important).   **Freezes about** 16°F.-28°F. for mature trees depending on variety.

pH Preference 5.5 to 7.0.   **Sun or Shade** Sun.

Rate of Growth Moderate.   **Salt Tolerance** Fair.

Culture Should be fertilized the same way as citrus trees—see citrus article. Avocados cannot stand "wet feet." Poor drainage will kill them. To avoid the cold, avocados on tender rootstocks may be planted deeper than other species of trees.

Propagation Wedge (cleft) and veneer grafting on young rootstock. Seedlings usually produce poor or no fruit. Top working or grafting is best done in December or January. Results are fair on to April.

Problems See article on avocados.

Varieties See article on avocados.

AVOCADOS

THE RACES OF AVOCADOS

It has been known for 300 years that there are three types of avocados based on location.

Races   ) 1. West Indian—though not native, intro. 1600
of   ) 2. Guatemalan
Avocados   ) 3. Mexican

	West Indian	Guatemalan	Mexican
Foliage	No Odor	No Odor	Anise odor
Native	Under 3,000 ft. Low Lands (Columbia & S. Am.)	3,000 - 6,000 ft. Highlands of C. Am.	Over 6,000 ft. Highlands of Mexico and Central America
Season of Fruiting	Summer & Early Fall	Winter & Spring	Summer
Months to Mature	5 to 8 Months	10 to 15 Months	5 to 6 Months
Skin Texture	Leathery, Pliable 1/16" Thick	Woody Tissue, Breaks Easily, 1/8" Thick	Papery Thin 1/32" Thick
Skin Color	Green-Red	Green-Red	Green-Black (Purple)
Hardiness - Cold	24° to 28°F.	21° to 26°F.	16° to 24°F.
Stem Length	Short Fruit Stem	Fruit Stem 3" to 5"	Short Fruit Stem
Seed Size	2 Seed Coats Larger Seeds	Small	Medium
Surface Character	Seed May Become Loose. Smooth	Rough - Ridges or Pebbled	Smooth

Avocado Varieties For Florida

Hardy Avocados For North and Central Florida

Variety	Flower Type	Race	Picking Dates	Fruit Color and Size	Fruit Quality	Freezes at about	Yield	Tree Size and Shape
Young or Mexicola	A	M	July-Aug.	Black 6 oz.	Fair	18°F.	Good	Medium tall
Gainesville	A	M	July-Aug.	Green 8 oz.	Fair	18°F.	Light	Medium tall

Less Hardy Avocados — OK For Central Florida Most Years

Variety	Flower Type	Race	Picking Dates	Fruit Color and Size	Fruit Quality	Freezes at about	Yield	Tree Size and Shape
Brogdon	A & B	M x WI	July-Sept.	Black 8-14 oz.	Very good	22°F.	Good	Medium tall
Winter Mexican	B	M x WI	Oct.-Dec.	Green 12-16 oz.	Good	22°F.	Good	Large well shaped
Lulu	A	G x WI	Oct.-Jan.	Green 14-24 oz.	Good	25°F.	Good	Tall thin
Taylor	A	G	Nov.-Jan.	Green 12-18 oz.	Very good	25°F.	Light	Tall upright
Monroe	A	G x WI	Nov.-Dec.	Green 24-40 oz.	Very good	26°F.	Good	Medium
Choquette	A	G x WI	Nov.-Feb.	Green 24-40 oz.	Very good	26°F.	Good	Medium spreading
Tonnage	B	G	Sept.-Oct.	Green 14-24 oz.	Very good	26°F.	Moderate	Tall upright

More Tender Avocados — For South Florida
In Central Florida — For Protected Areas Only

Variety	Flower Type	Race	Picking Dates	Fruit Color and Size	Fruit Quality	Freezes at about	Yield	Tree Size and Shape
Booth 7	B	G x WI	Oct.-Nov.	Green 10-20 oz.	Good	28°F.	Moderate	Medium spreading
Booth 8	B	G x WI	Oct.-Nov.	Green 9-20 oz.	Fair	28°F.	Heavy	Medium small spreading
Hall	B	G x WI	Oct.-Nov.	Green 20-30 oz.	Good	28°F.	Heavy	Medium
Pollock	B	WI	July-Sept.	Green 18-40 oz.	Very good	32°F.	Light	Medium spreading
Simmonds	A	WI	July-Sept.	Green 16-34 oz.	Very good	32°F.	Heavy	Medium spreading

Avocados are listed in the three charts above according to their cold tolerances.

PESTS OF AVOCADOS

Avocados are attacked by several scale insects such as pyriform, Florida red, and wax scale. Please look in the book **Florida Insects** for pictures and controls of these scale insects.

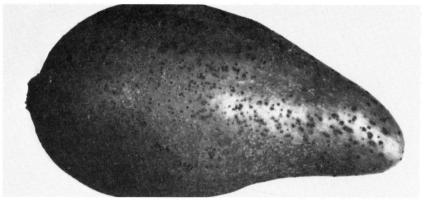

CERCOSPORA FRUIT SPOT

Avocados are also troubled by fungus diseases. One of these is cercospora fruit spot.

AVOCADO SCAB

Another more serious disease is avocado scab which attacks both the leaves and fruit.

ANTHRACNOSE

Anthracnose or black rot is also a prevalent disease on avocados. This disease is often seen as black rotting areas on and in fruit as they reach maturity.

A spray schedule to control the diseases mentioned should be carried on each year. Neutral copper can be used according to directions, or a nutritional spray containing copper, manganese and zinc should be used.

The first spray should be made when the bloom buds begin to swell. This is usually about late January.

The second spray should be made during late bloom when many of the fruit have set. This is usually about mid-February to March 15.

The third spray should be made about 3 to 4 weeks later or about mid-April.

A fourth spray will be needed in areas where cercospora and anthracnose are serious problems. This spray should be about mid-May.

POLLINATION OF AVOCADOS

It seems that all avocados except Collinson are self fruitful.

Other avocado varieties although self fruitful will probably bear more fruit regularly if A and B types are planted. (This is not necessary with the Mexican varieties as one isolated tree usually bears well.)

Avocados are unique in that they have A and B types of flowers, and they function as follows:

The A type flower opens the first morning as female. The stamens shed no pollen, but the pistil (stigmatic surface) is receptive to pollen. This flower closes at noon. This same flower reopens the next afternoon as male.

The B type flower opens as female the first afternoon, and usually closes at night and reopens as male the next morning.

stamens closed   pistil open   stamens open   pistil closed

A type A.M.   B type P.M.   A type P.M.   B type A.M

Which boils down to the fact that flowers shedding pollen (male) in the morning are B type while those that are shedding pollen (male) in the afternoon are A type.

76

Scientific Name Pouteria campechiana   **Family** Sapotaceae

INCHES

Common Name Egg-Fruit   **Native to** Central America
Canistel

Habit of Growth Evergreen, open tree   **Florida Height** 25' **Width** 25'

Description Leaves 4" to 8" long clustered near ends of twigs. Has clear milky sap. Flowers on new growth.

Fruit (Description & Use) Varies in shape from round to top-shaped. Skin orange-yellow and thin. Flesh dry like yolk of an egg. Eaten fresh and in pies.

Flower & Season Greenish-white, small clusters. May-August.   **Fruit Season** Sept.-March

Soil & Moisture Fertile, well-drained.   **Freezes about** 28°F.

pH Preference 5.5 to 7.5.   **Sun or Shade** Sun.

Rate of Growth Moderate.   **Salt Tolerance** Fair to good.

Culture Easy to grow with minimal care. Treat like citrus. Will grow on sandy or shallow limestone soils. Wind resistant tree.

Propagation Seeds take 3 to 6 months to germinate. To graft girdle the scion (budwood) about a month before grafting.

Problems Scale insects and rust disease.

Varieties Hume variety has larger fruit of better quality. Flesh not as dry.

INCHES

Common Name Peach   **Native to** China
Nectarine

Habit of Growth Small, open tree.   **Florida Height** 20′ **Width** 15′

Description Leaves long, slender, smooth, with fine serrate edges. Deciduous.

Fruit (Description & Use) Peach fruit fuzzy. Roundish with peak. Seed pitted and wrinkled. Nectarine fruit smooth.   Eaten fresh or cooked.

Flower & Season Solitary, pink. Varies with variety.

Fruit Season Late April to June.

Soil & Moisture Well-drained soils.

Freezes about 27°F. for fruit and flower. Tree hardy.

pH Preference 6.0 to 6.5.

Sun or Shade Sun.

Rate of Growth Moderate.

Salt Tolerance Poor.

Culture Prune each winter; take out crowded branches; cut back top growth and keep center of tree open to the sun. Thin to one fruit 5 to 8 inches apart along branch.

Propagation Should be on Okinawa or Nemaguard rootstocks. T-Budding in June.

Problems See article on peaches.

Varieties Picture is of Prunus persica var. nectarina (Sunred Nectarine).

GROWING PEACHES IN FLORIDA
By Lewis S. Maxwell

As a boy raised in central Florida, I well remember the large peach orchards that used to be in the Umatilla area. However, after a few years they were abandoned because of nematode damage.

Then for years those of us who loved peaches would eat the fruit of occasional seedling peaches or the small but excellent flavored Jewel peach. Many years later the Red Ceylon peach was introduced. It was somewhat larger than the Jewel peach, but nematodes were still the factor limiting our peach growing. This pest caused our peach trees to decline and die after three to five years.

Our first real break-through in peach growing came when two nematode resistant rootstocks were introduced. These were the Okinawa and Nemaguard and are now the only two rootstocks recommended as rootstocks for Florida peaches.

Our second break-through in growing Florida peaches was the work done by Mr. R. H. Sharpe in breeding peaches especially adapted to our Florida conditions.

If you want to be successful growing peaches in Florida, you must take into account the varying amounts of winter chilling that are necessary to allow good dormancy break and heavy fruit set of the different varieties of peaches. The number of hours of chilling needed is known as the chilling requirement of the variety of peach. The average number of hours of temperature below 45°F. that occurs in a normal year in the area determines whether the chilling requirement can be fulfilled for the variety of peach. There are other factors involved, but this rule works reasonably well.

To help you decide which peach varieties will grow best in your area study the map and the table.

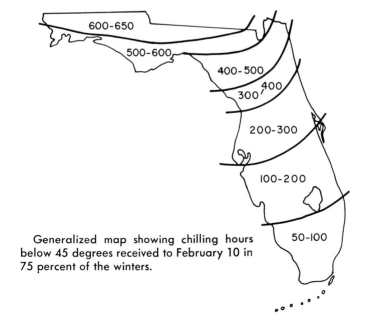

Generalized map showing chilling hours below 45 degrees received to February 10 in 75 percent of the winters.

TABLE — Variety Characteristics

	Normal Ripening Date*	Flesh Color	Flesh Firmness	Approx. Chilling Required
FlordaGrande	Mid-May	Yellow	Medium	50
Flordaprince	Late April	Yellow	Firm	100
Flordaglo	Early May	White	Firm	150
TropicBeauty	Early May	Yellow	Firm	150
TropicSweet	Mid-May	Yellow	Medium	175
TropicSnow	Mid-May	White	Medium	225
Sunblaze Nectarine	Mid-May	Yellow	Firm	250
Flordagold	Mid-May	Yellow	Firm	325
Flordacrest	Early May	Yellow	Firm	350
Sundollar Nectarine	Early May	Yellow	Firm	350
Flordaking	Early May	Yellow	Medium	400
Sungem Nectarine	Early May	Yellow	Medium	400
Sunlite Nectarine	Mid-May	Yellow	Medium	450
Flordaglobe	Early May	Yellow	Firm	450
Sunfre Nectarine	Early June	Yellow	Firm	525
June Gold	Mid-May	Yellow	Firm	650

*Ripening periods vary considerably with season. Dates given are considered normal for the areas where the varieties are best adapted.

Table prepared from information provided by Dr. W. B. Sherman, Florida Agricultural Experiment Stations, University of Florida, Gainesville.

This table gives pertinent information on varieties of peaches that can be grown in various parts of the State. For instance, the FlordaGrande peach usually ripens its fruit in Mid-May, and its fruit has yellow flesh. Its flesh is medium. The last column lists its approximate chilling requirement at 50 hours. By looking at both the map and the table, you will note that the FlordaGrande and Flordaprince peaches are the only peaches that will fruit well in the area south of a line drawn across the State at the southern end of Lake Okeechobee.

FERTILIZING

On the recommended rootstock, I have never found peaches hard to grow. I feed them similar to the way I do citrus except I feed them about ½ pound of fertilizer to each foot of tree spread (5 pounds each application to a tree with a spread of 10 feet). They should be fed three times each year— in late May, in mid-August, and a final feeding in mid-December. There are on the market some excellent peach tree special fertilizers. I use a quality fertilizer containing natural organics and added essential elements. I have never found copper in the fertilizer to damage my peach trees.

INSECT PESTS

WHITE PEACH SCALE

White peach scale is difficult to control. Spray your trees with oil plus Malathion twice, 14 days apart. Apply these sprays during the winter when your trees are most dormant. One spraying of oil plus Malathion during the winter will usually control San Jose scale. If either of these scales is severe during the summer, use a small paint brush to apply oil plus Malathion at spray strength over the scales.

PLUM CURCULIO

In areas of Florida where wild plums grow, plum curculio (a small weevil) is usually a pest. The female cuts a crescent-shaped mark when she lays her eggs. The larva is small, white, and legless, and it has a distinct brown head. To control this pest spray with recommended rates of both Sevin and Malathion. The first spray should be about 10 to 14 days after the petals have fallen. The second spray should be about 7 to 10 days later and the final spray about 12 to 14 days after the second spray. This spray program will also control plant bugs which distort the fruit (catfacing).

CARIBBEAN FRUIT FLY

This is a brown fly a little larger than a house fly. It has mottled wings. Those of you who live in south and central Florida face a relatively new pest. If you find small, whitish, apparently headless maggots in your fruit, they are probably the immature of the Caribbean fruit fly, Anastrepha suspensa. At present we do not have a control for this pest.

Sometimes the peach tree borer attacks the trunk of peach or plum trees usually near the soil line. This pest is the larva of a clear winged moth. You should scrape away the gum at the soil line and use a stiff wire to destroy the larva.

PEACH DISEASES

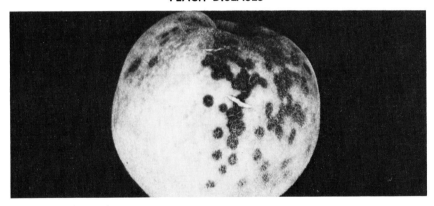

PEACH SCAB

This fungus disease can usually be controlled by adding Captan or wettable sulphur to your plum curculio sprays.

The longer your trees retain their leaves, the longer they will grow, and the more fruit they will produce. Rust causes much defoliation in central Florida. It is a good idea to spray your peach trees a couple of times with a neutral copper spray during the summer when rust is observed.

Since peach trees are usually deficient in zinc, nutritional sprays containing zinc will be helpful.

Now don't despair for we have discussed more problems than any of you are likely to have in growing peaches and nectarines. What is important is that you will receive many pleasures from picking and eating fresh peaches from your own tree. Plant several — growing your own fruit is fun.

Scientific Name Psidium littorale
(P. cattleianum)

Family Myrtaceae

Common Name Cattley Guava
Strawberry Guava

Native to Brazil

Habit of Growth Attractive, bushy shrub.

Florida Height 25' **Width** 15'

Description Leaves smooth, glossy, and deep green, 1½" to 3½" long. Young leaves are reddish. Has smooth bark which peels.

Fruit (Description & Use) Rounded, reddish, with persistent calyx. To 1½". Has many hard seeds. Fruit mildly sub-acid, pleasant.

Eaten fresh, in jams and jellies

Flower & Season White, 1" across. April-May.

Fruit Season June-August Occasionally any time of year.

Soil & Moisture Tolerant.

Freezes about 24°F.

pH Preference 5.5 to 7.5.

Sun or Shade Sun.

Rate of Growth Moderate.

Salt Tolerance Good.

Culture Should have adequate water as fruit mature. Very attractive ornamental shrub or hedge plant.

Propagation Usually by seed that come true to type.

Problems Red-banded thrips.

Varieties Yellow Cattley, P. littorale var. lucidum, has larger and sweeter fruit.

Scientific Name Psidium guajava   **Family** Myrtaceae

INCHES

Common Name Guava

Native to Tropical America

Habit of Growth Large bush or open tree.

Florida Height 25' **Width** 20'

Description Leaves large, coarse, opposite, with many prominent veins. Young wood 4-angled. Bark reddish-brown, flakes off revealing smooth gray bark.

Fruit (Description & Use) From round to pear-shaped. Skin smooth and waxy. Skin and pulp vary in color from yellow, white, to pink. Small hard seeds. Eaten fresh, in preserves and cooked.

Flower & Season White 1" across. April-May.

Fruit Season July-Sept. Also intermittent fruiting.

Soil & Moisture Tolerant.

Freezes about 29°F. Will come back.

pH Preference 5.5 to 7.0.

Sun or Shade Sun.

Rate of Growth Rapid.

Salt Tolerance Fair.

Culture Fertilize same as citrus trees. Judicial pruning will improve shape of tree.

Propagation Air layering, grafting, or by seeds. Seeds must be planted as soon as taken from the fruit. Cuttings will root under mist.

Problems Leaf roller caterpillar attack terminal leaf buds. Trees often zinc deficient.

Varieties Pink Indian, Ruby, Supreme, Patillo, Red Cross, and White Cross.

84

Scientific Name Punica granatum   **Family** Punicaceae

INCHES

Common Name Pomegranate

Native to Southern Asia

Habit of Growth Small, shrubby tree.

Florida Height 15' **Width** 8'

Description Suckers freely from base. Spines are sometimes found on seedlings. Leaves to 3" long, shiny. Deciduous.

Fruit (Description & Use) Roundish, yellowish to bright red. Has leathery skin and persistent tubular calyx. Seeds are covered with crisp, juicy, sub-acid pulp.   Eaten fresh.

Flower & Season Showy, orange-red, to 1½". April-June

Fruit Season All year in south Florida. July-Nov.

Soil & Moisture Any well-drained soil.

Freezes about 18°F.

pH Preference 5.5 to 7.0.

Sun or Shade Sun.

Rate of Growth Moderate.

Salt Tolerance Poor.

Culture Does best in areas that do not have humid summers. Not very satisfactory on lower east coast. Fruit poor on shallow limestone soils.

Propagation Seeds germinate in about 45 days. Superior varieties are grown from air layers or cuttings.

Problems Leaf spot disease on fruit and leaves. Fruit often split on tree. Best to pick fruit before they ripen. Suckers at base of plant require constant pruning.

Varieties Wonderful, Spanish Ruby, and others for fruit or flower.

85

Scientific Name Pyrus lecontei   **Family** Rosaceae

INCHES

Common Name Pear   **Native to** China

Habit of Growth Upright, deciduous tree.   **Florida Height** 20′ **Width** 25′

Description Tree erect except when in fruit. Often bends and branches may break. Trees self fruitful. (Fruit should be picked and ripened indoors.)

Fruit (Description & Use) Most pears grown in Florida are "cooking" pears. They have persistent calyx, thin skin and hard, white, grainy flesh.
Eaten cooked.

Flower & Season White, showy clusters. Late winter.

Fruit Season Early fall.

Soil & Moisture Well-drained, sandy.

Freezes about Hardy in Florida.

pH Preference 5.0 to 7.0.

Sun or Shade Sun.

Rate of Growth Vigorous first 10 years.

Salt Tolerance Very poor.

Culture Mulching beneficial. Do not over fertilize mature trees. Use low nitrogen and high potash fertilizers. Grows best north and north-central Florida.

Propagation By cuttings, grafting, and budding.

Problems Fire-blight, anthracnose, and several leaf spot diseases.

Varieties Hood, Baldwin, Orient have crisp, white flesh good as fresh fruit. Pineapple or Sand Pear is the most common cooking pear.

86

Scientific Name Rhodomyrtus tomentosa   **Family** Myrtaceae

INCHES

Common Name Downy-Myrtle   **Native to** Japan and China

Habit of Growth Attractive, ornamental shrub.   **Florida Height** 8′ **Width** 8′

Description Leaves opposite, green above, downy and gray below, 2½″ long. Venation of leaf unique.

Fruit (Description & Use) Roundish, ½″ diameter, dark purple in color. Calyx persistent. Prolific. Has many small seeds. Eaten fresh, in preserves and pies.

Flower & Season Rose-pink, attractive. ¾″. April-June.

Fruit Season June till Sept.

Soil & Moisture Moist, acid soil.

Freezes about 27°F.

pH Preference 5.5 to 6.5.

Sun or Shade Sun or light shade.

Rate of Growth Moderate.

Salt Tolerance Fairly good.

Culture Easy to grow. Resents heavy fertilization. Excellent medium-sized shrub for landscape use. When in bloom it is one of Florida's showiest fruiting plants.

Propagation From seeds or cuttings. Cuttings will produce fruit in about two years.

Problems No serious pests. Not well adapted to shallow limestone soils.

Varieties None known.

87

INCHES

Common Name Mysore Raspberry   **Native to** India

Habit of Growth Semi-vining bush.   **Florida Height** 6' **Width—**

Description Leaves alternate, pinnately compound. Leaflets dark green above, silvery below. Canes are whitish and thorny.

Fruit (Description & Use) Typical cone or thimble of drupelets. Purplish-black with whitish bloom, to ¾" diameter. Juicy, sweet, flavorful.

Eaten fresh, in juice and preserves

Flower & Season Showy pink on new growth. Dec.-May on each new flush.

Fruit Season Jan.-June. Heaviest Mar.-April. Occasional fruit to October.

Freezes about 29°F.

Soil & Moisture Enriched, well-drained.

pH Preference 6.0 to 7.5.

Sun or Shade Sun.

Rate of Growth Rapid.

Salt Tolerance Poor.

Culture Head back in Sept. to 4' or 5'. Cut back old canes to half their length after they have fruited. They need ample fertilizer. Require a support.

Propagation Easy to grow from seeds. Tip layerings or 2 node cuttings do best in late summer. However, cuttings can be made any time of the year.

Problems Use copper if anthracnose occurs. Stink bugs attack ripe fruit. As plantings get old, make more plantings on new soil.

Varieties None known.

Scientific Name Rubus hybrid　　　　　　　　　　**Family** Rosaceae

INCHES

Common Name Blackberry　　　　　　**Native to** N. E. United States

Habit of Growth Semi-erect suckering bush.　　**Florida Height** 4' **Width** 4'

Description Thorny plants similar to native blackberry only are larger and more vigorous. Leaves serrate, dark green.

Fruit (Description & Use) Typical, very large, blackberry.
　　　　　　　　　　　　　　Eaten fresh, in preserves and pies.

Flower & Season White with light pink flush. Mid-March to April.　　**Fruit Season** May-June.

Soil & Moisture Rich, moist soil.　　**Freezes about** 26°F.
　　　　　　　　　　　　　　Young berries 28°F.

pH Preference 5.5 to 7.0.　　**Sun or Shade** Sun.

Rate of Growth Rapid.　　**Salt Tolerance** Poor.

Culture Plant Brazos about 4' apart. Brazos is self-fertile — one plant will fruit. No trellis needed.

Propagation Best method is to use 4" to 5" leafy stem cuttings under mist. Use new canes while growth is still soft.

Problems Sprays are needed to control thrips and sometimes anthracnose. Double blossom or rosette, a fungus disease, sometimes attacks Brazos.

Varieties Brazos, Oklawaha, and Flordagrand.

89

Scientific Name Spondias cytherea   **Family** Anacardiaceae

INCHES

Common Name Ambarella
Otaheite-Apple

Native to Society Islands

Habit of Growth Large, spreading tree.

Florida Height 40′ **Width** 40′

Description Leaves pinnately compound, 8″ to 30″ long, clustered at the tips of thick branches. Leaflets shiny, bright green. Semideciduous.

Fruit (Description & Use) Oval with a tough, orange-yellow skin. Flavor varies from sweet to acid. Juicy flesh with single, spiny seed.
Eaten fresh, in preserves and sauces.

Flower & Season Small, whitish, terminal panicles. March-April.

Fruit Season Oct.-Jan.

Soil & Moisture Moderately fertile.

Freezes about 30°F.

pH Preference 5.5 to 7.5.

Sun or Shade Sun.

Rate of Growth Moderate.

Salt Tolerance Poor.

Culture Easily grown. Young plants grow very fast first 2 to 3 years. Best tasting of all the Spondias.

Propagation By seeds, which germinate in about a month, or by air layering. Also by very large 2″ to 3″ diameter cuttings and shield budding.

Problems No serious pests.

Varieties There are some superior clones but no named varieties are available.

90

Scientific Name Vaccinium spp. **Family** Ericaceae

Common Name Blueberry

Habit of Growth Mostly upright - some spreading. Shrub or small tree.

Native to S. E. United States

Florida Height 6'-20' **Width** 3'-8'

Description Leaves alternate, simple, elliptic-lanceolate to ovate, entire, to 3" long. Deciduous.

Fruit (Description & Use) A multiseeded berry with pigments in skin. Used fresh and in pastries.

Flower & Season White, pink to dark purplish, to ⅜" long. February.

Soil & Moisture Moist, flatwoods type soil.

pH Preference 4.0 to 5.5.

Rate of Growth Moderate.

Fruit Season May and June.

Freezes about 29°F. Hardy when dormant.

Sun or Shade Sun.

Salt Tolerance Poor.

Culture Shallow roots so no tilling. Limited root system so weed control is essential. Should be mulched.

Propagation Softwood and hardwood cuttings.

Problems Since most cultivars are self unfruitful, two or more cultivars should be planted together. Birds eat them.

Varieties Highbush-tetraploid: Sharpblue, Flordablue, and Avonblue. Rabbiteye-hexaploid: Aliceblue, Beckyblue, Bluegem, Woodard, Delite, Climax, Bonita, Choice, Chaucer, and Tifblue. Chilling hours: Aliceblue 300, Woodard 400, Tifblue 650.

FRY

Common Name Muscadine Grape   **Native to** Southeastern U.S.A.

Habit of Growth Climbing vine.   **Florida Height** 8' **Width** 25'-35'

Description (Variety Magoon) Vines medium vigor; shiny rounded leaves and regularly toothed margins, wood gray color with prominent lenticels.

Fruit (Description & Use) Purple, round berries with tough skins. Pulp juicy, sweet, excellent flavor.   Eaten fresh, in juice, wine, and jelly.

Flower & Season Self-fertile. May.   **Fruit Season** August.

Soil & Moisture Well-drained, moist.   **Freezes about** 15°F.

pH Preference 6.0 to 6.5.   **Sun or Shade** Full sun.

Rate of Growth Slow, then vigorous.   **Salt Tolerance** Poor.

Culture Overhead arbor best but single wire fence trellis acceptable. Fertilize as in grape article. Clean cultivation until trunk sizes.

Propagation Layers made in July will form roots before winter. Cut off and plant rooted layers in new location during dormancy (December to March).

Spray Program See article on muscadine grapes. Insect control is seldom needed.

Varieties See article on muscadine grapes.

MUSCADINE GRAPES

One of the best and easiest to grow of all fruit for the average home owner is the muscadine grape as it is well adapted to Florida.

The newer varieties have far better flavor, and the grapes are larger. Also, they bear more fruit than the older varieties.

The muscadine grape is native to the southeastern section of the U.S.A. and Florida. Many varieties are resistant to Pierce's Disease which makes the growing of European or Northern bunch grapes impossible in Florida.

PLANTING: Choose a spot where the grape vines will have full sun. Drainage should be good but not excessive. These grapes must be irrigated, especially when young.

The pH of the soil should be from 6.0 to 6.5. This may require adding dolomitic limestone. (Usually about three pounds to each 100 sq. ft. area will be sufficient.)

The grape vine should be planted in a well prepared planting hole.

Bare rootstock must be planted while dormant. This is usually from November 15 to April. However, grape vines growing in containers can be planted at any time.

TRELLISING: Muscadine grapes must have a strong support. This can consist of two 9 gauge galvanized wires about three and five feet from the ground. They require strong posts. However, some people still use an arbor. Bulletins are available from your county agent on trellising, training and pruning.

We must stress though that these vines must be pruned each winter while dormant. The main vines or "arms" are permanent, but the shoots are cut back to three or four buds each year while dormant.

Suckers should be cut off when found, and tendrils should not be permitted to wrap around and girdle the vine.

FERTILIZING: Muscadines should be well fed as they are vigorous, hungry plants. Beginning when growth starts, they should be fed monthly. The first year ¼ pound of a quality general purpose or citrus fertilizer containing organic nitrogen and added essential elements should be used for each vine for each feeding. The fertilizer should be scattered around the base of the vine, at least one foot from the vine.

The second year the vine should be fed in March, May, and just after harvest, only this year a pound of fertilizer should be used for each feeding. The third year and from then on about 2½ pounds of fertilizer per vine each feeding should be used. The vines should not be fertilized after Sept. 15th.

CULTIVATING: The area around the base of the vine must be kept free of weeds. Cultivation must be shallow since the grape roots are near the surface.

PEST CONTROL: Muscadines are easier to grow than bunch grapes. Muscadines should be sprayed with a neutral copper spray every two weeks, from the time flowers appear until the fruit begin to ripen. Spraying is to prevent fruit rots and leaf spots and is most important during the rainy season.

An insecticide such as Malathion or Sevin should be added at any time that insect pests are present except when the vines are in bloom as this would kill the pollinating insects.

The vines will be healthier and produce a better crop next year if the spray program is continued every two weeks until the end of the rainy season.

MUSCADINE GRAPES

VARIETIES: There has been some outstanding breeding work done on muscadine grapes during the last few years. Be sure and plant some of the new improved varieties. Many of these are self-fruitful, and one vine will produce abundant crops. However, some of the female varieties have such outstanding characteristics such as size of fruit, flavor, vigor, etc. that anyone contemplating having several vines should include some of the outstanding female varieties. The self-pollinating varieties will also pollinate the female varieties.

If a home owner in Florida had room for only one muscadine grape vine, a good one would be Southland. Fry and plant some of the new improved varieties. Many of these would be a good choice for a second vine as it is a female and so would be pollinated by Southland. Since it is susceptible to fruit rot, it will have to be sprayed.

If you cannot find muscadine grapes for sale at your local nursery, write to the Agricultural Research Center, P. O. Box 388, Leesburg, Florida 32748 for a list of nurseries that sell grapes.

	Flavor	Color	Size	Yield	Pollination	Vigor	Single or Clusters	Disease Resistance	Ripening	Ripens in Florida
SOUTHLAND	Very good	Black	Large	Very high	Self	Good	Clusters	Good	Even	Late midseason
FRY	Very good	Bronze	Very large	Very high	Female	Good	Clusters	Fair	Uneven	Early
COWART	Good	Black	Large	Good	Self	Good	Clusters	Good	Uneven	Midseason
DIXIE	Good, Sweet	Bronze	Large	Very high	Self	Very good	Clusters	Good	Even	Midseason
JUMBO	Good, Sweet	Black	Very large	Fair	Female	Very good	Single	Good	Uneven	Early midseason
HIGGINS	Good	Pink	Very large	Very high	Female	Very good	Clusters	Fair	Uneven	Late midseason
SUMMIT	Very good	Bronze	Large	Good	Female	Good	Clusters	Good	Even	Late midseason
WELDER	Good	Bronze	Medium	Very high	Self	Very good	Clusters	Good	Uneven	Midseason
TRIUMPH	Good	Bronze	Large	Very high	Self	Good	Clusters	Good	Uneven	Midseason
ALBEMARLE	Very good	Black	Large	Fair	Self	Good	Mostly singles	Good	Even	Early midseason

Scientific Name Vitis simpsoni-labrusca   **Family** Vitaceae

INCHES

Common Name Lake Emerald   **Native to** Central Florida
Habit of Growth Climbing vine.   **Florida Height** 6'-8' **Width** 20'-40'

Description Vine bears 3 to 6 long canes, 15' to 20' long, and several other
  shorter canes. A dense, wide canopy is formed from lateral growth. Leaves
  4½"x5", tough.

Fruit (Description & Use) Green fruit turns golden when ripe. Berry ½" to ¾"
  in diameter in dense bunches   Eaten fresh, in grape syrup, jelly and wine.

Flower & Season Self-fertile. April.   **Fruit Season** Late July.

Soil & Moisture Widely adapted.   **Freezes about** 28°F. depending on
                                               shoot tenderness.

pH Preference 5.5 to 6.5.   **Sun or Shade** Full sun.

Rate of Growth Rapid and vigorous.   **Salt Tolerance** Poor.

Culture Avoid crowding vines with ornamentals or shade trees. Clean cultivation until vines fruit; then clean cultivation each season until fruit harvest,
  followed by fall cover crop. Fertilize as in grape article.

Propagation By rooting hardwood cuttings about 12" to 15" long taken in
  January. Plants grow well on their own roots. Also by ground layers and
  root cuttings.

Spray Program About 5 or 6 fungicide sprays from the time bud growth begins until fruit reaches full size. Be sure to spray when in full bloom.

INCHES

Common Name Blue Lake   **Native to** Central Florida

Habit of Growth Climbing vine.   **Florida Height** 6'-8' **Width** 12'-25'

Description Large dark green leaves, nearly round, and disease-resistant. Leaves form a dense cover for the fruit crop, protecting from sunburn and bird damage.

Fruit (Description & Use) Purple to blue grape about ½" in diameter. When ripe, spicy and slightly tart. Berries must be fully ripe to be sweet.

Eaten fresh, in juice and jelly.

Flower & Season Self-fertile. April.   **Fruit Season** July (midseason).

Soil & Moisture Widely adapted.   **Freezes about** 28°F. depending on shoot tenderness.

pH Preference 5.5 to 6.5.   **Sun or Shade** Full sun.

Rate of Growth Rapid and vigorous.   **Salt Tolerance** Poor.

Culture Avoid crowding vines with ornamentals or shade trees. Clean cultivation until vines fruit; then clean cultivation each season until fruit harvest, followed by fall cover crop. Fertilize as in grape article.

Propagation By hardwood cuttings about 12"-15" long. Plants grow well on their own roots.

Spray Program About 5 or 6 fungicide sprays from time bud growth begins until fruit reaches full size. Be sure to spray when in full bloom.

BUNCH GRAPES

The grapes Lake Emerald, Blue Lake, Conquistador, Daytona, Suwannee, and Stover are suited to the growing conditions of Florida, except for the southeast coast. They are resistant to Pierce's Disease. The first two grapes are pictured and discussed on the preceding pages.

Conquistador is a purple, Concord-flavored variety, self fertile, and useful for fresh juice, jelly and red wine. It is best when grafted on a resistant rootstock such as Tampa or Dog Ridge.

Daytona is a pink table grape with a meaty texture, large bunches and berries. Anthracnose susceptibility requires attention with regular fungicidal sprays.

Suwannee is a golden grape useful for fresh market or white wine. This variety develops a slight muscat or spicy flavor that is pleasing to the taste.

Stover is a light green grape useful for fresh eating or white neutral flavored wine. It is best when grafted on a resistant rootstock such as Tampa or Lake Emerald.

There are grape diseases that must be controlled before grapes can be grown successfully. These are discussed below.

DOWNY MILDEW

Patches of gray fungus fruiting bodies in spots on the undersides of the leaves are the first symptoms seen. Most areas on the leaves where this "down" occurs will become brown. Downy Mildew is probably the most common leaf spotting disease on grape leaves.

BLACK ROT

Black rot first shows up on grape leaves as dark brown lesions. They are usually round in shape. This disease is serious because later, if it is not controlled, it will cause the grapes to rot.

ANTHRACNOSE

Anthracnose is another disease of grape vines. It appears as malformed leaves and lesions on the grape vines.

Fortunately downy mildew, black rot, and anthracnose can be controlled with fungicides. Use benomyl or a neutral copper spray. In order to control these fungus diseases, a preventive program is necessary. The spray program must begin when the first green shoots are seen in the spring.

The spray program is as follows:

The first green shoots should be sprayed when they are about three inches long, and then without fail the vines and leaves should be sprayed thoroughly every two weeks for six or seven times.

If malathion plus Sevin is added to the spray, it will control leafhoppers, aphids, and the grape leaf folder.

GRAPE LEAF FOLDER

In planting young grape vines a planting hole should be prepared by mixing thoroughly into the soil one shovelful of compost. The grape vine can then be planted. A generous amount of water should be used in order that no air pockets are left around the roots. The vine should be watered every other day for the first two weeks and never allowed to suffer from drought.

The first year, soon after spring growth begins, apply one quarter pound of a 6-6-6 or 8-8-8 fertilizer with 20% to 30% of the nitrogen from natural organic sources, in two lateral bands a foot away from the vine. Repeat this application in May, June, and early September.

The second year apply one pound of the same fertilizer in February, May, and just after harvest. Rates can be increased in future years but should not exceed four pounds per vine per year. Split applications are more efficient than a single application.

Weed control is essential to allow maximum benefit to be received from fertilization and irrigation.

Aegle marmelos   BAEL FRUIT

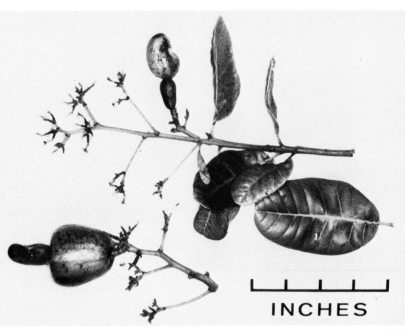

Anacardium occidentale   CASHEW

INCHES

Annona cherimola   CHERIMOYA

INCHES

Byrsonima crassifolia   GOLDEN SPOON

101

INCHES

Castanea pumila   CHINQUAPIN

Cereus peruvianus

INCHES

Clausena lansium   WAMPI

INCHES

Coccoloba uvifera   SEA-GRAPE

Elaeagnus philippinensis   LINGARO

Harpephyllum caffrum   KAFIR-PLUM

Hovenia dulcis   JAPANESE RAISIN-TREE

Myrciaria glomerata

Parmentiera edulis

GUAJILOTE

Pouteria hypoglauca

INCHES

Rheedia aristata

Rollinia spp.

WILD SWEETSOP

INCHES

Synsepalum dulcificum   MIRACLE FRUIT

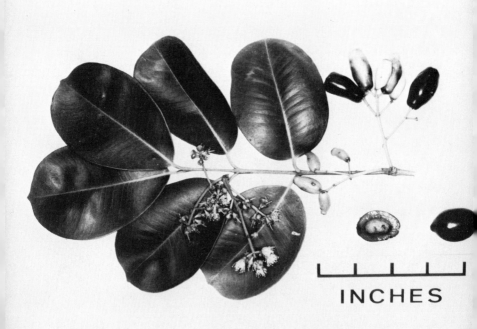

INCHES

Syzygium cuminii   JAMBOLAN-PLUM, JAVA-PLUM

108

Syzygium jambos   ROSE-APPLE

Syzygium malaccensis   MALAY-APPLE

109

From "Fifty Tropical Fruits of Nassau" by Kendal & Julia Morton.

Ximenia americana   **TALLOW-WOOD**

Zizyphus mauritiana   **INDIAN JUJUBE**

Morus spp.   MULBERRY

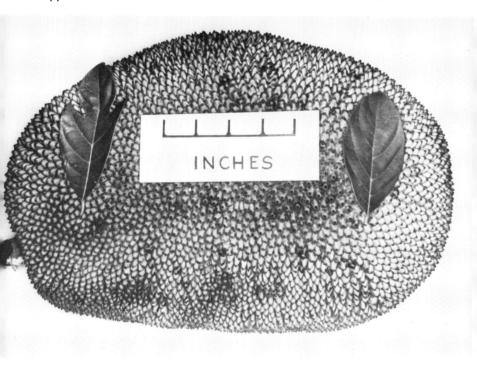

Artocarpus heterophyllus   JAKFRUIT or JACKFRUIT

Tamarindus indica   TAMARIND

Monstera deliciosa   CERIMAN

PRUNING
By A. H. Krezdorn

Pruning is a complex topic and various species differ widely in their requirements. Grapes, for example, are cut back to a few buds each year while citrus goes unpruned until it crowds. Thus, discussion here is limited to a few principles.

REASONS FOR PRUNING

Many deciduous fruits are pruned to form strong, wide-angled crotches. This is done by cutting back side-branches the first year so the trunk grows faster than the branches.

Some trees are pruned to reduce the number of fruits and to form fruits on vigorous, new growth. This causes larger fruits. Peaches, particularly, respond to this.

Most evergreen trees such as citrus, avocados and mangoes are pruned primarily to keep the tree from getting too large. Commercially, the tops and sides of these trees are periodically cut back with huge mechanical saws. The trees are, in effect, huge hedges. In the dooryard, it is more effective to keep such trees in bounds by selectively removing branches as the tree outgrows its allotted space.

RESPONSES TO PRUNING

There are two types of pruning. Thinning out is the complete removal of a branch or twig. The branch is cut off flush at the point it is attached to another one. Heading back is cutting off a branch part way rather than to its point of attachment.

Heading back results in the stimulation of growth of buds on the remaining stub and vigorous new shoots. Thinning out results in very little new growth. This is generally true regardless of the size of the branch.

The reason for this is that bud growth is locally inhibited by growth regulators contained in the newly developing leaves of shoot tips. Removing part of the branch removes this inhibitor and buds below it are forced into growing. Cutting off a complete branch destroys not only the source of inhibitors but all of the buds that are inhibited.

It is important to understand these two responses and to use them appropriately. A tree can be kept in bounds with less work by emphasizing thinning out instead of heading back. On the other hand, old trees can often be rejuvenated by heading back large limbs.

TIME OF PRUNING

Deciduous fruit trees are usually pruned in the winter when leaves are off the tree and it is dormant. Prune in late winter to avoid early growth and possible frost damage.

Pruning evergreen species is best done in winter just before flowering; however, it can be done at almost any time of the year, particularly if only occasional branches are being thinned out. Avoid heavy pruning in the fall that will stimulate growth and render the tree tender to cold.

REMOVING SUCKERS

Suckers and water sprouts continuously arise from the roots and trunks of trees. They should be removed annually. This is best done by occasionally rubbing them off with a gloved hand when they first arise. Otherwise, they should be pruned off flush with their point of attachment.

 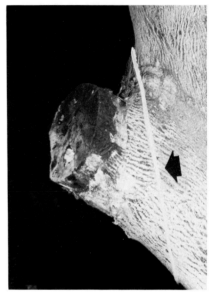

PREVENTING SPLIT BRANCH   **AVOIDING STUB**

REMOVING A LARGE BRANCH

Thinning out or completely removing a large branch requires three cuts. (See photograph.) First, undercut the branch about a foot from its point of attachment. Then cut from the top a few inches farther out. This will prevent splitting of the branch and damage to the limb or trunk to which it is attached. Then cut off the stub flush. Leaving a short stub results in rotting.

Heading back a large branch is done in the same manner except the cuts are made farther out and the third cut is made the desired distance out from the branch's point of attachment. The third cut should be made square with the plane of growth. One can often see slight bumps on large branches that are evidences of buried, dormant buds. Cutting back to such bumps ensures growth near the cut and good healing.

WOUND DRESSING

Wound dressings or paints are not usually necessary, as evidenced by the millions of untreated cuts made each year in commercial pruning of Florida's citrus and other fruits. In fact, use of the common black asphalt paints on cuts of large branches exposed to the sun can inhibit healing. However, large cuts close to the soil that are prone to infection can be covered with either a black asphalt paint or a thick cover of white latex paint. (Do not use any paint containing lead.) A wound dressing of this sort can prevent the entrance of diseases and insects and prevent the drying and cracking of the woody center of the wound. Common wound dressings are not antiseptic and do not promote healing.

FLORIDA'S CLIMATE
By A. H. Krezdorn

Florida is a peninsular state with a variety of climatic zones. The northern part of the State, while too warm for all varieties of temperate zone fruits, has winters sufficiently cool to produce commercial peaches, blueberries, grapes, plums, pecans and even apples. Moreover, such fruits can be produced as dooryard fruits in most parts of the State. Varieties of deciduous or temperate zone fruits must, however, be carefully chosen on the basis of their chilling requirement; i.e., the hours of winter temperatures 40°F. or below needed for proper flowering and fruiting. It is also important not to choose varieties with chilling requirements too low for a given zone because they will flower too early and the blossoms will be frozen.

Central and parts of southern Florida contain the world's most productive citrus plantings. Moreover, certain types of hardy citrus can be grown in the northern part of the State, and virtually all citrus can be grown as a dooryard fruit as far south as Key West. The best quality of oranges are grown in central Florida because the cooler climate enhances their color and flavor. Some tender types of citrus are limited to the warmest parts of the State.

Tropical fruits such as avocados, mangoes, papayas, pineapple, bananas and myriads of minor species are limited to extreme southern Florida; however, they can be grown close to both coasts as far north as Bradenton on the west and to Ft. Pierce on the east. Of course, some of the tropical fruits can be grown in especially warm sites in the central parts of the State. In this respect, it is important to understand that there are many microclimates in Florida where differences in elevation, nearness to lakes (especially the south side of the large lakes), and protection from buildings and other structures greatly affect the warmth of the location.

Rainfall is relatively heavy, particularly in the summer and the humidity is high. This coupled with the mild temperatures is conducive to growth of diseases, insects and weeds. None of these factors are, however, limiting.

Hurricanes occasionally cause damage but neither are they limiting. Large commercial plantings of tropical fruits exist in even those areas most prone to hurricanes. Beach front homes are often subjected to protracted winds that are highly damaging. Tall, salt tolerant hedges afford considerable protection in such cases.

COLD PROTECTION OF PLANTS

Freezing temperatures usually occur in Florida on calm, clear nights; however, a few occur with a blowing wind. During the day, in either case, the soil and trees are warmed by heat radiating from the sun, and a reservoir or bank of heat is built-up in the soil. The soil absorbs more heat if it is free from weeds and grass and when it is wet and the surface well packed rather than cultivated. At night the soil radiates heat into space and cools because none is being received from the sun. If there is no wind, the warmer air in contact with the soil loses heat to the cooler earth by conduction and a temperature inversion develops; i.e., the air aloft is warmer than that next to the earth. If the cooling persists, air temperature will drop below freezing, and the depth of the inversion will increase until the entire plant is in freezing air. Heat also is being lost from the tree parts by radiation, and the upper leaves exposed to the sky may become as much as 10°F. colder than the air.

A wind of only a few miles an hour will mix the air, prevent inversion and delay the drop in air temperature. This is the principle of wind machines.

Mulches and weeds act as insulators against the earth. They prevent absorption of heat during the day and its loss at night, both of which contribute to freeze damage, the former because it reduces heat build-up in the earth and the latter because the tree does not receive as much radiation heat from the soil at night.

A dense canopy of leaves traps the heat radiating from the soil beneath it and keeps the trunk and inner part of the tree warmer than the outside on calm nights.

A cloud cover on calm nights absorbs heat radiating from the earth and radiates it back. Therefore, a damaging freeze rarely occurs on a cloudy, calm night.

Similarly, placing covers of blankets, corrugated paper boxes and other material over plants both entraps heat from the soil and prevents losses of heat by radiation from the plant. Covers are very effective and are made virtually frost proof if a burning electric light bulb is placed under the cover. Plants placed under heavily foliated trees are in effect "covered" and considerable protection is afforded. Covers furnish protection during both calm and windy freezes.

Heaters and fires are effective on clear calm nights if the flame is low. Protection comes from the hot gases filling the space below the inversion layer. Burning heaters at high burning rates blasts hot gases through the inversion layer. Cold air is thereby sucked in from outside the heated area, and the heating is ineffective. On the other hand, the burning rate must be high on windy nights because the hot gases are blown away and radiant heat from the glowing heaters is the only effective heat produced.

Plants can be afforded complete protection by keeping them covered with a freezing mixture of ice and water due to the heat released when water freezes. However, if insufficient water is applied, the sprinklers applying the water freeze-up or the water source fails, evaporative cooling from the ice surface occurs and it is colder under the ice than if no ice were present. Water can be turned off as soon as air temperatures two to three degrees above freezing is reached the next day. One serious problem with water is that excess ice loads which break the tree limbs may occur in freeze durations of over an hour or two. One should understand the use of water and have a perfect system, or more damage may occur than if water had not been used.

Trunks of young trees may be protected by banking soil around them in the late fall and removing it after danger of frost has past. The soil should be free of organic material, such as weeds, to prevent rotting of the bark. Commercial tree wraps and tying heavy quantities of dry straw or other materials around the trunk also afford some protection but less than that of soil banks.

Healthy, well-fertilized plants will tolerate more cold than diseased or nutritionally weak ones. Care should be taken not to over fertilize and water or to apply fertilizer so late that the plant's winter dormancy is delayed. Plants of many species, such as citrus, become much hardier to cold when dormant (the bark is not slipping) than when they are not. A week of warm weather in the winter can render citrus much more tender to cold even though no shoot elongation or bud swell takes place. Also, unshaded trunks of deciduous trees, such as peaches, may lose their dormancy or the southwest side of the tree due to intense sunlight. Then a freeze will kill the active tissue. Wrapping the trunk or painting it white offers considerable protection by keeping the trunk from absorbing heat on sunny days.

CUBAN NAMES OF TROPICAL FRUIT

By Al Will, Jr.

Scientific Name	Common Name	Cuban Name
Anacardium excelsum	Cashew	Espave, Nariz
A. occidentale	Cashew	Maranon
Ananas comosus	Pineapple	Pina
Annona diversifolia	Ilama	Ilama
A. glabra	Pond-Apple	Boga, Corcha
A. muricata	Soursop	Guanabana
A. purpurea		Cabeza de negro
A. reticulata	Custard-Apple	Corazon de buey, Mamon
A. squamosa	Sugar-Apple	Anon
Artocarpus communis	Breadfruit	Arbol del pan
A. heterophyllus	Jakfruit, Jackfruit	Jac Jaca
Averrhoa bilimbi	Bilimbi	Calamias Camias
A. carambola	Carambola	Carambola
Bertholletia excelsa	Brazil-nut	Coquito del Brasil
Blighia sapida	Akee	Seso Vegetal
Bromelia pinguin	Pinguin	Pina de raton
Brosimum alicastrum	Breadnut	Guaimaro
Byrsonima crassifolia	Golden Spoon	Palo de gallina
Calocarpum sapota	Mamey Sapote	Mamey colorado
Carissa carandas	Karanda	Karanda
Casimiroa edulis	White Sapote	Mango tarango
Chrysobalanus icaco	Coco-Plum	Hicaco de costa, Hicaco
Chrysophyllum cainito	Star-Apple	Caimito, Camito blanco
Clausena lansium	Wampi	Lansio, Wampi
Coccoloba uvifera	Sea-Grape	Una caleta
Diospyros discolor	Velvet-Apple	Mabolo
D. kaki	Japanese Persimmon	Kaki del Japon
Dovyalis caffra	Kei-Apple	Manzana de Kei
D. hebecarpa	Ceylon-Gooseberry	Ketambila
Durio zibethinus	Durian	Erizo de arbol
Elaeagnus philippinensis	Lingaro	Lingaro
Eriobotrya japonica	Loquat	Nispero del Japon
Eugenia dombeyi	Grumichama	Grumixameira
E. malaccensis	Malay-Apple	Pomarrosa de Malaca
E. uniflora	Surinam-Cherry	Cerezo de cayena
Euphoria longana	Longan	Longan
Feijoa sellowiana	Pineapple-Guava	Guavasteen
Ficus carica	Fig	Higo, Higuera
Flacourtia indica	Governors-Plum Ramontchi	Ciruela de Madagascar, Ciruela del gobernador

Scientific Name	Common Name	Cuban Name
Fortunella japonica	Kumquat	Naranjita japonesa
Garcinia mangostana	Mangosteen	Mangostan
G. tinctoria		Rata-Gorake
Genipa americana	Marmaladebox Genip	Genipap, Jagua
Glycosmis pentaphylla	Orange-Berry	Naranjita de cristal
Litchi chinensis	Lychee	Leechee
Macadamia ternifolia	Queensland Nut	Nuez de Queensland
Malpighia glabra	Barbados-Cherry	Cereza del pais, Cerezo
Malus sp.	Apple	Manzano
Mammea americana	Mammee-Apple	Mamey de Santo Domingo
Manilkara zapota	**Sapodilla**	**Nispero, Chicle**
Melicocca bijuga	Spanish-Lime, Genip	Mamoncillo
Monstera deliciosa	Ceriman	Ceriman de Mejico
Morus sp.	Mulberry	Mora
Muntingia calabura	Strawberry-Tree	Capuli, Capulinas
Myrciaria cauliflora	Jaboticaba	Joboticaba
Passiflora edulis	Passion-Fruit	Ceibey, Granadilla
P. foetida		Caguajasa, Pasionaria
P. quadrangularis	Giant Granadilla	Granadilla Pasionaria
Persea americana	Avocado	Aguscate
Phyllanthus acidus	Otaheite-Gooseberry	Grosella, Manzana lora
P. emblica	Emblic	Mirobalanos emblicos
Pouteria campechiana	Egg-Fruit	Canistel
Prunus persica	Peach	Melocotonero
Psidium littorale	Cattley Guava	Guayabita cereza
	Strawberry Guava	
P. guajava	Guava	Guayaba
Punica granatum	Pomegranate	Granada
Rheedia aristata		Manaju
R. madruno		Madrono
Spondias cytherea	Otaheite-Apple	Caja Manga, Ciruela
	Ambarella	
S. mombin	Yellow Mombin	Ciruela agria
	Hog-Plum	
S. purpurea	Purple Mombin	Ciruela campechana
Syzgium cuminii	Java-Plum	Jambolana
S. jambos	Rose-Apple	Pomarrosa,
		Manzana de rosa
Tamarindus indica	Tamarind	Tamarindo
Triphasia trifolia	Lime-Berry	Limoncito
Vitis vinifera	Grape	Parra, Uva

Index Of Common Names Of Florida Fruit

This book is arranged alphabetically according to the scientific names of the fruit pictured and described. This index is arranged alphabetically according to their common names.

Florida GARDEN GUIDE

OVER 2,750,000 PRINTED

Available from—

FREE IN MOST AREAS OF FLORIDA

Published in January, March, May, July, September, and November

PUBLISHED BY LEWIS S. MAXWELL, B.S.A. • 6230 TRAVIS BOULEVARD • TAMPA, FLORIDA 33610

Copyright © LEWIS S. MAXWELL and BETTY M. MAXWELL

WHAT TO DO IN YOUR GARDEN

In January

In Florida on some warm moist day in January, we often see our first flight of flying termites. Termites are a serious problem in the warm areas of the world.

If termites or suspicious insects are seen, call your termite specialist at once. Controlling termites in the modern home is difficult and complicated and can only be accomplished by a qualified professional termite exterminator.

To make your annual flowers bloom better and longer, you should remove the old flowers. Some of the flowers from your annuals should be cut and used in the house for decorations. Fresh flowers are so attractive and brighten up the home. This cutting of part of the flowers will also help your annual flower plants to bloom longer and better.

Ryegrass and Bermudagrass should have an extra fertilization in January. These grasses do not go dormant and so need this extra feeding to keep them healthy and green.

Continue to protect your cold sensitive plants.

Roses, peaches, and grapes **must** be pruned back when they are most dormant if they are to produce an abundance of flowers or fruit.

Those of you who want to set out dormant trees, shrubs, or vines should do this now before it is too late.

At last there is an apple that will do well in central Florida. It is called "Anna" and was developed in Israel. It requires only 200 to 400 hours of under 45°F. for good production. You or your nurseryman may be able to get some of these from the Grand Island Nursery, Grand Island, Florida 32726. This is the only source that I know.

IT CAN HAPPEN HERE!

"The budget should be balanced; the Treasury should be refilled; the public debt should be reduced; the arrogance of officialdom should be tempered and controlled. Assistance to foreign lands should be curtailed lest we become bankrupt. The mob should be forced to work and not depend upon government for subsistence."

Marcus Tullius Cicero in Rome between 106 and 43 B.C.

In February

Fertilize your citrus, other fruit, and shade trees as well as woody shrubs this month. Feeding them now will have the fertilizer elements available when the trees need them for their spring growth. This feeding is necessary if you are to have fruit or beauty from your trees.

In Florida with its poor sandy soils, there is no substitute for a quality fertilizer containing organics and added essential elements. Only a quality fertilizer will completely feed your plants.

If your bearing citrus trees need shaping, deadwood removed, or suckers cut out, this should be done before the flush of growth that produces the bloom. Don't wait as late pruning can hurt your next crop.

Citrus trees especially grapefruit should be sprayed with a neutral copper spray to prevent Melanose. Read the inside pages of this FLORIDA GARDEN GUIDE for information regarding some citrus diseases. Also read the article on fertilization and care of citrus in the book FLORIDA FRUIT.

Cut back your poinsettias when they start to look ragged. These cuttings can be used to start more plants.

Spring comes to Florida about the middle of February. At this time we can start planting our warm weather vegetables and annual flowers. Look on the back page to find a planting guide. We seldom have a hard freeze after February 15th.

TOMATO HORNWORM

The March/April FLORIDA GARDEN GUIDE will feature an article "The Insect Pests of Vegetables." It will also give controls.

Since 1964 the FLORIDA GARDEN GUIDE © has been available FREE to gardeners in many areas of Florida.

This is an authoritative garden guide which is published every other month by Lewis S. Maxwell who is also publisher of the nine books described on the back cover of this book.

The FLORIDA GARDEN GUIDE is purchased by leading garden supply dealers, hardware stores, nurseries, termite specialists, and lawn spraymen to give as a FREE SERVICE to their customers to help them garden more effectively in Florida.

A file of these publications will make a valuable gardening reference.

There is now someone in many communities of central and south Florida who offers this service and who would appreciate your asking for it.

It is not available to individuals by subscription. With any inquiry regarding it, please send a stamped self-addressed envelope.

Lewis S. Maxwell, 6230 Travis Boulevard, Tampa, Florida 33610